Follow the map
the Ordnance Survey guide
by John G. Wilson

A & C Black · London
Ordnance Survey · Southampton

Contents

Introduction

Welcome to this guided tour of the world of maps from the Ordnance Survey—*the* mapmakers in Great Britain since 1791.

'Maps are for everyone' is the theme of this book. Not just for walkers and hikers—though there's plenty here for them—but also for motorists, cyclists, holidaymakers, canoeists . . . Whether you live in town or country, whether you have a hundred maps or one, you can gain a lot of practical help as well as pleasure from knowing how to use maps to the full.

These pages are packed with information about the whole range of Ordnance Survey maps and their usefulness to leisure users of all kinds. How to recognise the symbols used—how to find your way with the help of the map—how to spot fascinating landscape features and remains of our past—why Milton Keynes is so called . . . Any journey can become so much more interesting with a map, especially when you can 'see through' the contours and symbols to get a picture of the land surface over which your route lies.

If you're planning to visit outstanding areas of natural beauty such as the National Parks, or choosing a good holiday site, or going for a walk, or just browsing at home—come with us, and follow the map!

The challenge to the map maker: the rise and fall of the land and man's contribution to the landscape must be recorded on the map in fine detail, but everything must be easy to read.

Part I

MAPS AND MAPMAKERS

Chapter 1

The range of Ordnance Survey maps

View from the air

One cool clear morning in late summer, an aircraft flew north over the Home Counties. A camera clicked to record a vertical view of the land beneath. We share this view in the photograph opposite. It gives us a bird's eye view of a rural corner of Hertfordshire.

In the top right-hand corner, buildings of varied shapes and sizes straggle into the form of a village. Narrow country lanes twist and turn over a countryside seen in colours appropriate to the season. Trees are

Extract 1

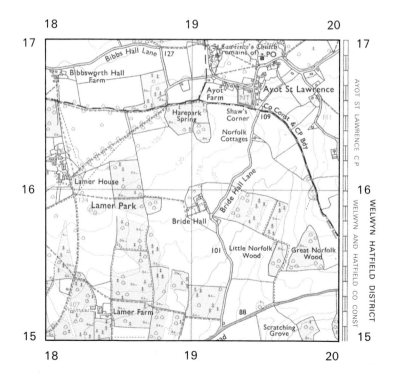

clustered into patches of woodland, dot the parkland around the village and shelter the isolated farms. Fields bear the varied hues and textures of busy agricultural use. It is a picture typical of much of rural England.

The map on the previous page (*extract 1*), like the photograph, takes a vertical point of view. It may lack the reality granted by natural colour, but it has more to offer. The printed word releases this small area from its anonymity. The village springs to life as Ayot St Lawrence, for long the home of George Bernard Shaw. It can be reached along Bride Hall or Bibbs Hall lanes. Great Norfolk Wood can be distinguished from the appropriately smaller Little Norfolk Wood. It is Lamer Farm that is enveloped in the woodland that clothes the bottom left-hand corner.

Much of interest is recorded on the map in the form of signs and symbols. A small black square topped by a cross locates the parish church of Ayot St Lawrence. The letters NT tell us that the home of the playwright is safe in the hands of the National Trust. Footpaths, often too faint to be picked out on film, are emphasised in broken lines of green or black. Items not to be seen on the ground, boundaries for instance, are clearly plotted on the map.

The map, though flat like the photograph, includes a vital third dimension. The pale orange number-labelled lines that wriggle over the face of the map are contour lines, which record the height of the land above the level of the sea. Correctly interpreted, they enable us to picture the rise and fall of the land surface—the raw material of scenery.

Scale
The map, like the photograph, must, of necessity, be much smaller than the land it portrays. A measure of this reduction is the *scale* of the map. The above extract is taken from the Ordnance Survey Pathfinder series. It is drawn to a scale of 1:25 000. All distances measured in the course of survey are divided by 25 000 before being plotted on the map. 1:25 000 is also known as the map's

representative ratio. It gives precise indication of the relationship between any measurement made on the map and its equivalent on the ground. It means that one unit of length on the map is equal to 25 000 such units on the ground. Thus, if a stretch of road measures 1 centimetre on a Pathfinder map, we can be certain that in reality it has a length of 25 000 centimetres (or, more practically, a quarter of a kilometre). Similarly, a footpath measuring four centimetres on the map will involve a walk of one kilometre.

The ratio 1:25 000 occupies a prominent position on the cover of all Pathfinder maps, and is useful in identifying the series. For practical purposes, however, the simple statement 'Four centimetres equals one kilometre', is a more meaningful way of expressing the scale of this useful map.

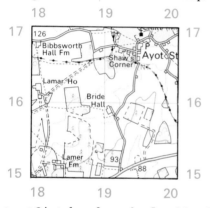

Extract 2

Extract 2 is taken from the flagship of the Ordnance Survey fleet—the Landranger series. Its scale is 1:50 000 or, as a simple statement, 'Two centimetres equals one kilometre'. Although the ratios may, at first sight, lead us to think otherwise, 1:50 000 is in fact a smaller scale than 1:25 000. The degree of reduction is greater. Consider, for instance, a road that is exactly one kilometre long. At a scale of 1:25 000 it will be represented on the map by a line of four centimetres. At a scale of 1:50 000, the line will be only half as long. *Extracts 1* and *2* portray exactly the same area of land, but the area of the 1:50 000 extract is only quarter of that of the 1:25 000 map. It is clear that at the larger scale the draughtsman has more space at his disposal, and can portray the land surface in much greater detail. This advantage has its price, however. A larger scale means that a smaller area of land can be mapped on a sheet of convenient size. If our movement is rapid, as in a car for instance, we soon pass beyond the margin and need the adjoining sheet. The map user must assess his requirements, and often make a choice between detail and convenience.

If the map is to tell its full story, the significance of scale must be fully appreciated. Perhaps it will prove helpful if we think of an aircraft on the final stages of its flight. As it nears its destination, it is flying high. As we look down through the cabin window, the ground seems exceedingly far away. Our view covers a wide expanse of the country, but detail is slight. We can pick out the line of the coast, and perhaps the shape of a major city, but little else can be identified. As the aircraft slowly loses height, occasional glimpses of the ground may be compared to a series of maps, of progressively larger scale. The area within our field of view becomes steadily more restricted. Gradually we are able to identify smaller and yet smaller features. Towns are seen, then villages, hamlets and finally individual houses. In similar sequence, estuaries, large rivers, streams and tiny brooks come into vision. If, amid the excitement and tension of the final approach, we can bear to glance down through the window, we gain a view that bears comparison with that of the largest large-scale map. We see only a tiny patch of land, but everything is clearly laid out beneath us.

The Ordnance Survey
The Ordnance Survey, as its name suggests, had a military origin. The threat of invasion by Napoleon's France highlighted Britain's lack of accurate maps, and the Ordnance Survey was founded, in 1791, to meet the need. The chosen scale was one inch to one mile, and the first sheet,

Extract 3

covering part of Kent, appeared in 1801.
Four years later a second sheet, this time of
part of Essex, was issued by the fledgling
Ordnance Survey, then safely housed in the
Tower of London. By the time the danger of
invasion had passed, only a handful of maps

were available, but their value was so widely appreciated that the survey was extended to cover the whole country. Progress was slow, and it was not until 1873 that the Ordnance Survey, by now an independent department of the Civil Service with headquarters in Southampton, could offer complete cover of England and Wales. Scotland had to wait a further fifteen years.

These early maps were printed in black from copper plates laboriously engraved by hand. A small extract from the earliest map is seen on the previous page. The first editions of these one inch to the mile maps are now of great historical interest. Britain has greatly changed since the date of the first survey, and each map gives an accurate and detailed picture of the land as it was over a hundred years ago. It is fascinating, especially for an area one knows well, to compare maps of past and present. The earliest maps are now collectors' items, but they have been reprinted, with useful notes, by David and Charles Ltd. of Brunel House, Forde Road, Newton Abbot, Devon, from whom further details may be obtained.

Throughout the present century, the Ordnance Survey has steadily extended the range and improved the quality of its output. New series of maps have been introduced at varying scales, and the introduction of colour printing has enhanced both appeal and clarity. In 1969, in response to the national movement towards metric units, the Ordnance Survey embarked upon a programme of complete metrication. This was a daunting prospect, for all sheets in all series of maps had to be converted to appropriate metric scales. The old well-loved 'one inch' map (1:63 360) for instance was replaced by the slightly larger-scale metric equivalent, 1:50 000. In addition, all information about the height of the land, which maps carry in profusion, had to be converted from feet to metres. The inevitable period of transition is now nearing its end. Virtually all OS maps are now drawn to convenient metric scales.

Metrication of heights, however, still has some way to go, and the Ordnance Survey continues to publish some maps on which the foot is the unit employed. The number is rapidly decreasing, but it will be 1990 before the lengthy task of metrication is finally completed.

Surveying and revision

Ordnance Survey maps are based on the precise results of a painstaking process of survey. A framework is provided by 25,000 control points known as 'triangulation stations', the position and height of which are determined with the greatest accuracy. By fine measurement of angles, the detail of the landscape is tightly tied to this essential and unique framework. Measurements are transferred to working drawings which slowly grow into the raw material of the published map.

It is a changing picture that the surveyor tries to capture on paper. The landscape that he views through his theodolite is subject to slow and sometimes significant change. Both nature and man make their contribution. Rivers, for instance, may shift

The setting sun highlights the shifting channels and sandbanks of Morecambe Bay.

their channels and build up new sandbanks where they meet the sea. Generally, however, nature's changes are imperceptible, and it is man that has the greater impact. A hedge that is here today may be gone tomorrow. Today's field of wheat may be tomorrow's housing estate. In a sense, every map is a historical document. It presents a picture of the land at a particular date, and this date is honestly recorded in the margin of each OS map.

Map revision is a constant concern of the Ordnance Survey as it endeavours to record the changing face of Britain. Close co-operation with local and national authorities brings advance warning of major developments. Aerial photography pin-points unsuspected changes which are then investigted by teams of surveyors who, in remote areas, may be taken to the site by helicopter. Modern technology helps speed the work of revision. The theodolite may be augmented by laser and infra-red measuring devices. The results of the surveyor's labours can be recorded in digital form in computers and stored on magnetic tapes or discs, and sophisticated machines can translate this stored data into drawings by means of an ultra-fine beam of light.

Modern methods make for fast and effective revision, and help to ensure that the published map is as up-to-date as possible

Maps in abundance

Today the Ordnance Survey publishes maps to meet every need. They are drawn to scales which range from large to small, from 1:1 250 to 1:625 000.

Large-scale maps

The maps of largest scale (1:1 250, or one centimetre to 12.5 metres) are only available for large towns, those with built-up areas of more than 1000 hectares, or populations greater than 20,000. Smaller urban areas, and land in close agricultural use, are mapped at 1:2 500 (one centimetre to 25 metres). On both series of maps, the amount of detail is truly impressive. Each building and fence is precisely plotted.

Roads are named and houses identified by number or name. The functions of other buildings are clearly stated. Such is the scale of these maps, that features as small as a bus shelter, a telephone call-box and even a pillar, pole or post can be shown. On the 1:2 500 maps the area of fields and other open spaces is given in hectares and acres. Maps at these large scales each cover but a small area of land. At 1:1 250 it is only 500 metres by 500 metres. They are of value mainly to professional specialists, civil engineers and town planners for example, who use accurate large-scale surveys in the course of their work.

The largest scale at which maps are available for the whole country, including its loneliest moorlands and highest mountains, is 1:10 000 (one centimetre to 100 metres). Each sheet represents 5 kilometres by 5 kilometres, and the scale is sufficiently large for the draughtsman to draw a full, clear picture of the natural and human features of the land surface. The sheet covering your local area can be of great interest and practical value, and may well provide some surprises.

Based on this series, the Ordnance Survey is publishing a growing list of colourful Town and City maps, which emphasise features of interest to residents and visitors alike. Roads are named and indexed, car parks and one-way road systems are indicated, and local services and amenities are highlighted.

Routeplanner and Routemaster maps

At the other extreme of the range of scales are maps mainly of interest to the motorist. The Routeplanner Map, at a scale of 1:625 000 (one centimetre to 6.25 kilometres) covers the whole country in a single sheet. At a scale of 1:250 000 (1 cm to 2·5 km), nine sheets are required for the Routemaster series. These show relief by subtle colour shading, and paint a broad regional picture on which all types of road are distinguished by colour and width of line. Further information of interest to the motorist is included.

Landranger maps

It is the OS maps which occupy the middle of the spectrum of scale which are of greatest interest to the greatest number of people. These, encountered above in *extracts 1* and *2*, are distinguished by name and scale. The Landranger has a scale of 1:50 000 (2 centimetres to 1 kilometre) and covers the country in 204 sheets, each representing an area of land some 40 kilometres by 40 kilometres. Most of these maps are available in a re-designed and updated second series.

Landranger maps record the length, breadth and height of the country in a degree of detail that is adequate for most purposes. They are of value to all who venture beyond the end of the street. To the motorist, for instance, they are a practical asset in several ways. In large, congested built-up areas, landmarks faithfully recorded on the map can guide him to his destination. In country districts he can select the shortest or prettiest route to a chosen attraction such as village, scenic view, ancient monument or caravan site.

Signposts guide the motorist to Luton; the OS map will show the way to a particular road or street.

The accurate road navigation that is possible with the aid of the Landranger is appreciated by rallyist, treasure hunter and tourist alike. These advantages are also appreciated by the cyclist, for whom the map's detailed information about the height and steepness of the land is of particular pedal-pushing interest.

Navigation is not normally a problem for those who travel on canals, but the location of canal-side amenities, public houses for instance, is an advantage for those who holiday inland yet afloat. Those who prefer a seaside holiday will also find a Landranger map a worthwhile investment. It provides a truthful picture of coast and beach, and suggests interesting walks or excursions in the vicinity.

The walker, be he stroller, rambler, hiker or back-packer, has long had an affection for the Landranger map and its famous 'one inch' predecessor. The recent inclusion of symbols for public rights of way, which the public are free to follow, has greatly enhanced the appeal.

Pathfinder maps

Rights of way are also shown on the Pathfinder maps (1:25 000), which are ideal for all who have an interest in the countryside. They do all that the Landranger does, and more besides, for their larger scale allows more detail to be included. Pathfinder maps come in two styles. The 'first series', which cover an area 10 kilometres by 10 kilometres, are rapidly being replaced by the more attractive second series Pathfinder maps, which usually cover twice the area. At this scale, even larger sheets are produced for districts of great attraction such as Snowdonia, the Lake District, the New Forest and the North York Moors. They cover 500 square kilometres or more, and are known as *Outdoor Leisure* maps.

Tourist maps

Finally, in describing maps of general usefulness, mention must be made of the short series of Tourist maps. At a scale of one inch to one mile, they represent the last significant remnant of mapping in imperial units. As will be appreciated from extract 14 (page 106) they are most attractive productions, and they have an added advantage in that they cover popular areas such as Dartmoor and the Peak District in single, handy sheets. One Tourist map, that of Snowdonia and Anglesey, is at a scale of half an inch to one mile.

Other maps

The Ordnance Survey also publishes a variety of maps of more specialist interest. Small-scale maps are available which indicate local government divisions, parliamentary constituency boundaries and petty sessions areas. A series of great archaeological and historical interest portrays Britain at significant periods from Ancient Britain to Monastic Times. A range of geological maps gives detailed information about Britain's firm foundation, the nature of the underlying rocks; while for agricultural purposes a series of soil maps specifies the characteristics of the soil.

The rich farming lowlands of the Severn Valley viewed from the Malvern Hills. Features of the landscape, both natural and man-made, are recorded on the map by means of signs and symbols.

Part II

READING
AND UNDERSTANDING

Chapter 2

Signs and symbols

Much of the information that the map contains is given in the form of so-called 'conventional signs'. These signs or symbols are subject to occasional slight change as the Ordnance Survey continues to update its specifications. Pages 26–27 give a full key to the signs used in the most recent editions of the Landranger series. It is an impressive array. Meanings are clear and precise, but some that are of particular value in rural areas deserve comment.

Photograph opposite To cross this stream near Hinxton, Cambs., the traveller has the choice of ford or bridge. The choice is recorded by symbol on the OS map.

Paths and rights of way
Of prime interest to the walker are the routes he is free to follow. On land of open access, much of which consists of high peaks and moorland within the National Parks, you are free to wander at will.

The stark surface of a limestone pavement. Ingleborough Hill broods in the background.

1:50 000 Second Series Map
CONVENTIONAL SIGNS

ROADS AND PATHS   Not necessarily rights of way

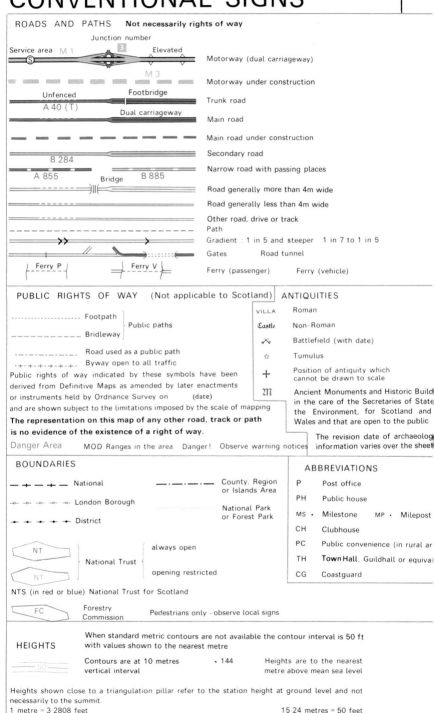

Junction number

Service area M 1   Elevated   Motorway (dual carriageway)

M 3   Motorway under construction

Unfenced   Footbridge   Trunk road
A 40 (T)

Dual carriageway   Main road

Main road under construction

B 284   Secondary road

A 855   Narrow road with passing places

Bridge   B 885

Road generally more than 4m wide

Road generally less than 4m wide

Other road, drive or track
Path

Gradient : 1 in 5 and steeper   1 in 7 to 1 in 5

Gates   Road tunnel

Ferry P   Ferry V   Ferry (passenger)   Ferry (vehicle)

PUBLIC RIGHTS OF WAY   (Not applicable to Scotland)

.... Footpath ⎫
                               ⎬ Public paths
_ _ _ _ _ _ _ _ Bridleway   ⎭

_.._.._.._.._.. Road used as a public path
·+·+·+·+·+·+· Byway open to all traffic

Public rights of way indicated by these symbols have been
derived from Definitive Maps as amended by later enactments
or instruments held by Ordnance Survey on   (date)
and are shown subject to the limitations imposed by the scale of mapping

**The representation on this map of any other road, track or path
is no evidence of the existence of a right of way.**

Danger Area   MOD Ranges in the area. Danger! Observe warning notices

ANTIQUITIES

VILLA	Roman
Castle	Non-Roman
⚔	Battlefield (with date)
☆	Tumulus
+	Position of antiquity which cannot be drawn to scale
₥	Ancient Monuments and Historic Build in the care of the Secretaries of State the Environment, for Scotland and Wales and that are open to the public

The revision date of archaeolog
information varies over the sheet

BOUNDARIES

_ + _ + _ National   _._._._ County, Region or Islands Area

_o_o_o_o_o_ London Borough

National Park
or Forest Park

_•_•_•_•_•_ District

NT   ⎫
     ⎬ National Trust ⎰ always open
NT   ⎭   ⎱ opening restricted

NTS (in red or blue) National Trust for Scotland

FC   Forestry Commission   Pedestrians only - observe local signs

ABBREVIATIONS

P	Post office
PH	Public house
MS •	Milestone MP • Milepost
CH	Clubhouse
PC	Public convenience (in rural ar
TH	**Town Hall**, Guildhall or equiva
CG	Coastguard

HEIGHTS

When standard metric contours are not available the contour interval is 50 ft
with values shown to the nearest metre

_50_   Contours are at 10 metres   • 144   Heights are to the nearest
       vertical interval   metre above mean sea level

Heights shown close to a triangulation pillar refer to the station height at ground level and not
necessarily to the summit.

1 metre = 3·2808 feet   15·24 metres = 50 feet

WATER FEATURES

	Marsh or salting		Slopes
	Lake		Cliff
	Canal, Lock and towpath		Flat rock
	Canal (dry)		Low water mark
	Aqueduct	Mud	High water mark
	Footbridge		
	Normal tidal limit	Sand	
	Lighthouse(in use and disused)	Dunes	
	Beacon	Shingle	

GENERAL FEATURES

	Electricity transmission line (with pylons spaced conventionally)		Radio or TV mast
	Pipe line (arrow indicates direction of flow)		Church or Chapel { with tower / with spire / without tower or spire }
ruin	Buildings		
	Public buildings (selected)	○	Chimney or tower
	Quarry		Glasshouse
	Spoil heap, refuse tip or dump		Graticule intersections at 5' intervals
		(H)	Heliport
	Coniferous wood	△	Triangulation pillar
	Non-coniferous wood		Windmill with or without sails
	Mixed wood		Windpump
	Orchard		Park or ornamental grounds

RAILWAYS

	Track multiple or single
	Track narrow gauge
	Freight line, siding or tramway
a b	Station (a) principal (b) closed to passengers
LC	Level crossing
	Embankment
	Cutting
	Bridges, Footbridge
	Tunnel
	Viaduct

ROCK FEATURES

outcrop   cliff   scree

TOURIST INFORMATION

🄸	Information Centre
	Selected places of tourist interest
	Viewpoint
𝒞	Public telephone
𝒞	Motoring organisation telephone
PC	Public convenience (in rural areas)
P	Parking
⊠	Picnic site
⋀	Camp site
	Caravan site
▲	Youth hostel
	Golf course or links
	Bus or coach station

and published by the Ordnance Survey, Southampton

Elsewhere, if trespass is to be avoided, you are advised to keep to public rights of way.

Britain has an intricate network of public paths. The total length is more than 200,000 kilometres. It is possible to stride from Land's End to John o'Groats without recourse to a surfaced road. Many paths are of great antiquity. The walker who treads the long-distance Ridgeway Path, is, at least in part, following the footsteps of prehistoric man. Long stretches of once Roman roads have declined to the status of footpath. The majority of paths were established in the dark ages between the departure of the Romans and the Norman Conquest, when much new land was first cleared of forest and converted to agriculture, and when movement was mainly on foot. They linked village to farmland and village to village.

Under the National Park and Access to the Countryside Act of 1949, local authorities have the task of recording all rights of way, and recording them on a 'definitive map'. It is from this source that the Ordnance Survey obtains its local information that is needed for the accurate updating of rights of way. If the information is not as yet complete, the fact is recorded in a diagram in the margin of the map.

Symbols

Rights of way come in three main categories, and on the 1:50 000 maps each has its distinctive symbol in *red*. Footpaths—small dashes on the latest maps—are for walkers only. Larger dashes indicate bridleways which may be followed on horseback or on pedal-cycle as well as on foot. Alternate short and long dashes represent a 'road used as a public path', which has, in fact, the same opportunities for use as a bridleway. A fourth category has made its appearance on the most recent maps, where alternate small crosses and dashes indicate a 'byway that is open to all traffic'.

A right of way, as its name suggests, allows the public to cross what is usually private land. The course of the great majority is clearly visible on the ground, but it must be stressed that this is not always the case. Paths may become overgrown and disappear through lack of use. Farmers have the right to plough a path that crosses a field, provided they restore the path within six weeks. Sadly, this is not always done. The right of way still exists and is marked on the map, but to follow it may involve a discouragingly muddy tramp. In case of doubt, the Definitive Map of rights of way may be consulted at the offices of the local authority.

The Ordance Survey uses another symbol for a footpath—a line of short *black* dashes. These paths are there on the ground, but for some reason they do not carry a legal right of way. It is, however, extremely rare for the walker to be impeded in any manner when following one of these paths.

The map contains a wide variety of thin linear symbols, pecked or solid. They must be carefully distinguished, for in some circumstances, poor light for instance, confusion is possible. Walkers have been known to mistake the symbol for the boundary of an administrative district with that for a footpath. Confusion between the footpath right of way and the thin red line which marks the limits of National Trust and Forestry Commission properties has brought similar problems to less careful or knowledgeable map readers.

In Scotland, the law with regard to rights of way differs from that in England and Wales. Any path that links two public places—villages for example—is deemed to carry a public right of way. The same is true of any path that has been in continuous public use for twenty years. There is no statutory obligation on local authorities to prepare definitive maps. All paths in Scotland are shown on OS maps by the black dashes symbol. There is no guarantee that the public has a right of way, but it is only in exceptional circumstances that the walker will find his freedom restricted. One possible source of

Dent, North Yorkshire.

disappointment is that paths may be closed during the grouse-shooting season.

In recent years a number of long-distance footpaths have been established by negotiating new links between existing rights of way. They are not marked by any special symbol on Landranger maps, but at convenient intervals they are indicated by name, e.g. Ridgeway Path, or by the abbreviation LDP (long-distance path).

Tracks

The typical path is narrow and only bears traffic in single file. A track, in contrast, is a more prominent route, for it is usually wide enough to take a tractor. A pair of black lines, close and parallel, is the sign for a track, and if it is unbounded by hedge, fence or wall, the lines are broken into dashes. Tracks often give most pleasant conditions for walking. They offer gentle gradients and are easily followed. The going is particularly good in parts of the Pennines where a dry springy turf covers the native limestone rock.

Buildings

The Landranger map uses pale orange shading to indicate buildings. Public buildings such as hospitals and schools are outlined in black. Throughout Britain, buildings are clustered into settlements of varying size. At one end of the scale there is the lonely isolated farmhouse. At the other, the monstrous conurbations such as Birmingham and Manchester, which may occupy a whole map sheet or more. In large urban areas the resident finds the map a useful detailed guide, but for most map users it is settlements in rural areas that are of the greatest interest.

In small country towns, for instance, the map locates such features of practical value as rail and bus stations, information offices, youth hostels and so on. Villages are a common source of interest, either for a pause on a journey, or for the inherent attractions that many display. The map can tell us much. The pattern of buildings reveals the form of the village. This is frequently linear, as the buildings string out along a minor road or roads. It may be more compact, with buildings clustered together, possibly at a crossroads, or perhaps around the open space of a village green. The presence and type of church will be recorded (though not the denomination), as may the existence of useful services such as a public house or a post office which usually has the additional function of a general store. With knowledge of contours (see page 100) we can picture the setting of a village within the natural landscape, which often includes a nearby stream or river. The map, however, can say little about the relative charm of a particular village. This depends much on such fine detail as the age and style of the buildings and, of course, on the personal tastes of the visitor. The map can guide us to a village, but leaves us much to discover and enjoy.

Bretforton, a Worcestershire village on the site of an Anglo-Saxon settlement.

A small stream is swallowed up to continue its journey underground.

Tourist information

The Landranger maps include, in blue, information tailored to the needs of the tourist. Their usefulness is clearly evident. To find a place to park the car is often an essential prelude to an enjoyable day in the country. Features of interest such as waterfalls and nature trails, ancient monuments and historic houses are backed on the map by light blue shading, and may suggest intriguing destinations or give purpose and point to many a country walk.

Water and coastline

Blue is also the colour used for rivers, lakes and other water features. A thin blue line marks the course of a river in its infancy. The line thickens as the river widens, and when it reaches eight metres in width, it is represented by a double line infilled with a lighter shade of blue. Should the river eventually broaden out into a tidal estuary, the bounding blue lines are replaced by black, so that it becomes possible to identify the inland limit of the effect of tides. On maps of upland areas composed of limestone rock, the blue lines of river or stream may be interrupted or even stop abruptly. This is due, not to a slip of the draughtsman's pen, but to the ability of rivers to dissolve for themselves an underground course. Often the name of the hole that swallows them up is recorded.

The map gives a clear and accurate account of Britain's varied and attractive coastlines. It speaks through signs and symbols of the width of the beach, and of its composition, be it sand or mud, shingle or rock. It records sand-dunes, mudflats, saltmarsh and cliffs. The accessibility of a particular beach can be determined by the presence or otherwise of a road or path. Such information is of great value when planning a seaside holiday. The map is much more reliable than many a holiday brochure. A site often loses its appeal when it is found that the beach is narrow, composed of shingle, and can only be reached by following a tortuous path down a steep high cliff.

Danger signs

Map signs that speak of inconvenience, or even of danger, are not to be ignored.

Grassy sand dunes give way to salt marsh. Both are indicated on the map by 'conventional signs'.

especially by those who venture on to the wilder hillsides of Britain. Ministry of Defence firing ranges are an example. They are starkly labelled in red on the Landranger map, and local information must be sought before proceeding in these areas. Warning notes are also printed on maps covering dangerous areas such as Morecambe Bay where wide expanses of sand may be quickly engulfed by fast-flowing tides.

Marsh, indicated on the map by little blue bristles, is not restricted to level lowland. It is frequently found in upland country where rainfall is heavy and slopes are gentle. If a squelching trek is to be avoided, the map will suggest a wise detour.

Many upland areas were, in former times, actively worked for lead and other minerals. In such areas the surface may be scarred by pits and shafts. On the map, the warning sign is groups of small black circles.

Rock features
The presence of cliffs is recorded in black. Expected on the coastline, they are also frequently encountered in the depths of the country. They are often found high on hillsides where they mark the outcrop of a tough band of rock. Offering opportunities

High chalk cliffs form a backdrop to a shore of flat rock and shingle. This scene is accurately portrayed on the map by means of conventional signs.

to climb and scramble, they are magnets to many. To others they are barriers to be avoided, and when cloud is low and light is poor, they can be a source of danger. Distinctive black shadings record other rock features such as bare outcrops and scree. The latter is, perhaps, the least familiar. In aprons of sharp angular rock fragments, scree lies at the foot of the steep slopes from which the fragments have been prised by rain and frost. Scree is often seen as a tempting line of descent from high ridges and peaks, but care is needed. The loose fragments tend to move faster than feet, and sharp rock can make a painful impression. To ascend a scree is slow and tedious, for it is usually a case of two steps up and one step down.

A view of Roulston Scar, North Yorkshire, from Sutton Bank.

1:25 000 Second Series Map (Metric
CONVENTIONAL SIGNS

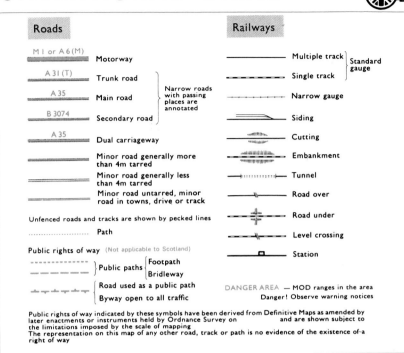

Roads

M 1 or A 6 (M)	Motorway
A 31 (T)	Trunk road
A 35	Main road
B 3074	Secondary road
A 35	Dual carriageway

Narrow roads with passing places are annotated (Trunk road, Main road, Secondary road)

Minor road generally more than 4m tarred

Minor road generally less than 4m tarred

Minor road untarred, minor road in towns, drive or track

Unfenced roads and tracks are shown by pecked lines

.... Path

Public rights of way (Not applicable to Scotland)

Public paths { Footpath / Bridleway }

Road used as a public path

Byway open to all traffic

Public rights of way indicated by these symbols have been derived from Definitive Maps as amended by later enactments or instruments held by Ordnance Survey on   and are shown subject to the limitations imposed by the scale of mapping
The representation on this map of any other road, track or path is no evidence of the existence of a right of way

Railways

Multiple track	Standard gauge
Single track	Standard gauge
Narrow gauge	
Siding	
Cutting	
Embankment	
Tunnel	
Road over	
Road under	
Level crossing	
Station	

DANGER AREA — MOD ranges in the area
Danger! Observe warning notices

Abbreviations

BP	Boundary Post
BS	Boundary Stone
CH	Club House
F	Ferry { Foot
V	Vehicle }
FB	Foot Bridge
Ho	House
MP	Mile Post
MS	Mile Stone
Mon	Monument
P	Post office
Pol Sta	Police Station
PC	Public Convenience
PH	Public House
Sch	School
Spr	Spring
T	Telephone, public
A	Telephone, AA
R	Telephone, RAC
TH	Town Hall
Twr	Tower
W	Well
Wd Pn	Wind Pump
Y	Youth hostel

P, Pol Sta, PC, PH — Rural areas only

Vegetation

	Coniferous trees
	Non coniferous trees
	Coppice
	Orchard
	Scrub
	Bracken
	Heath
	Rough grassland
	Reeds
	Marsh
	Saltings

Bracken, Heath, Rough grassland — Shown collectively as Rough Grassland on some sheets

Reeds, Marsh — Shown collectively as Rough Grassland on some sheets

NB. Due to changes in specification there are differences on some earlier sheets

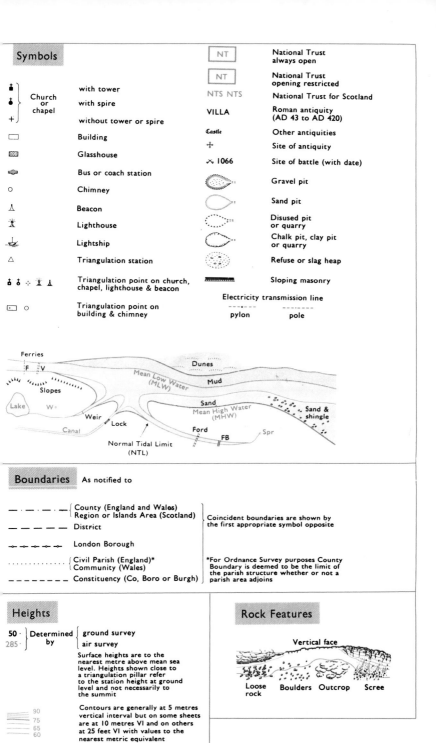

Symbols

Church or chapel	with tower	NT	National Trust always open
	with spire	NT	National Trust opening restricted
	without tower or spire	NTS NTS	National Trust for Scotland
	Building	VILLA	Roman antiquity (AD 43 to AD 420)
	Glasshouse	Castle	Other antiquities
	Bus or coach station		Site of antiquity
	Chimney	⚔ 1066	Site of battle (with date)
	Beacon		Gravel pit
	Lighthouse		Sand pit
	Lightship		Disused pit or quarry
	Triangulation station		Chalk pit, clay pit or quarry
	Triangulation point on church, chapel, lighthouse & beacon		Refuse or slag heap
	Triangulation point on building & chimney		Sloping masonry

Electricity transmission line

pylon   pole

Ferries

Dunes

Mean Low Water (MLW)

Mud

Slopes

Lake

Sand

Mean High Water (MHW)

Sand & shingle

Weir

Lock

Canal

Ford

FB

Spr

Normal Tidal Limit (NTL)

Boundaries   As notified to

—·—·—·— County (England and Wales) Region or Islands Area (Scotland)	Coincident boundaries are shown by the first appropriate symbol opposite
— — — — District	
—◆—◆—◆— London Borough	
.... Civil Parish (England)* Community (Wales)	*For Ordnance Survey purposes County Boundary is deemed to be the limit of the parish structure whether or not a parish area adjoins
— — — — — Constituency (Co, Boro or Burgh)	

Heights

50· 285·	Determined by	ground survey
		air survey

Surface heights are to the nearest metre above mean sea level. Heights shown close to a triangulation pillar refer to the station height at ground level and not necessarily to the summit

90
75
65
60

Contours are generally at 5 metres vertical interval but on some sheets are at 10 metres VI and on others at 25 feet VI with values to the nearest metric equivalent

1 metre = 3·2808 feet

Rock Features

Vertical face

Loose rock   Boulders   Outcrop   Scree

Pathfinder signs and symbols

The conventional signs used on the Pathfinder maps are presented on pages 36–37. They bear a family resemblance to those of the Landranger series, but colour is often different. Rights of way, for instance, are shown in green. Because of the larger scale of these maps, greater detail is possible, and this is particularly so with regard to vegetation and rock features.

Field boundaries

For walkers, a major asset of the Pathfinder maps is the inclusion of field boundaries. Every field is defined by thin black lines. In gentle lowlands, boundaries are typically thick-set hedges, often studded with mature trees. With their flowers and wild life they can add charm and interest to a country walk. In harsh upland areas, hedges give way to stone walls, reflecting in their colour the nature of the underlying rock. Walls in limestone areas, the Derbyshire Peak District for instance, gleam white in the sunshine. On neighbouring gritstone, walls are, in contrast, dark and dour. Many of these walls are of great age. Without the binding force of mortar, they have withstood the test of time and weather. They are less resistant to clambering boots, however, and considerate walkers always use the stiles and gates, whose variety makes them a source of interest in themselves.

Field boundaries are of great practical value to the walker, for they serve as a close-knit set of reference points. The path can be traced along or across each and every field, and your position can be easily and precisely checked. If an eye is kept on the Pathfinder map, it is difficult to lose your way.

Knowing the signs

Familiarity with conventional signs is important if one is to appreciate all that the map has to say. This familiarity may be achieved by the pleasant pastime of 'map browsing'. Let your eye wander idly over

the map, and translate the symbols as you meet them. You soon build up a detailed mental picture of the fascinating countryside that the map portrays.

View from the Long Mynd, Shropshire, looking west towards the Welsh border.

Chapter 3

Place names

An essential requirement of any map is, of course, to name the towns, villages and hamlets that it locates. For this the Ordnance Survey uses a variety of type, the size of which reflects the area of individual settlements. Similarly the status of natural features such as hills and valleys, moors and fens is reflected in the size and spacing of the type employed. Illustration is provided below.

Place names have an intrinsic fascination. They can be intriguing, amusing and the source of endless speculation. Few eyebrows will be unraised when an eye, wandering over *extract 10* (page 99), alights on the villages of Lower and Upper Slaughter. Names such as Crutch, Cricket, Pickup, Piddle, Tuttle, Tottle, Spittle, Shottle, to say nothing of Oswaldtwistle, Rubbery, Leatherhead,

A selection of type faces used in the 1:50 000 series.

Towns 10–20 km² in area 2–5 km² in area 0–2 km² in area	**RUGBY** **KENILWORTH** **THRAPSTON**
Suburban areas Over 1 km²	Shirley
Villages Over ½ km² in area Under ¼ km² in area	Hythe Beaulieu
Hamlet	Five Houses
Farm	Bury Fm

Towns	
30–50 km² in area	**LUTON**
0.5–2 km² in area	Thrapston
Villages	
Average size village	Flamstead
Hamlet	Nomansland
Farm	Hillend Farm
Lakes, bays & islands	
2–10 km² in area	**Bay of Firth**
Rivers	
Single, less than 4 km long	River Ver

Ipplepen and Blubberhouses may be the source of mild amusement, except perhaps to their inhabitants. Some place names have a poetic touch. Names such as Appleby Magna, Hazlebury Bryan, Sturminster Newton and Winterbourne Abbas trip lightly off the tongue and almost beg to be set to music.

A selection of type faces used in the 1:25 000 series.

The meanings of place names
A name newly encountered on map or

The beauty of Wendens Ambo, Essex, is matched by the charm of its name.

signpost prompts us to ponder its meaning. We are right to assume that Battle is the site of a battle—the so-called battle of Hastings, 1066 and all that. Teignmouth is situated at the mouth of the river Teign. The name Ashwood means what it says. Oxford is indeed the site of a ford once used by oxen.

Seldom, however, can a place name be so simply and accurately interpreted. Redcar, Sparrowpit, Newbottle, Crumplehorn, Herodsfoot and Bonehill, to quote but a handful of examples, are names which do not mean what they appear to mean. Names such as Chippenham, Whippingham and Effingham lead to wild and fanciful speculation which may at least have the merit of passing the time on a long car journey.

All the names of places and natural features which appear on the OS map once had a meaning. Names were chosen by practical people for practical purposes and were descriptive and clearly understood by all. But place names, with few exceptions, have great antiquity. Most date back over a thousand years. Some are more than twice as old. The names of the majority of English settlements are inscribed in the Doomsday Book which was completed in 1086. With the passage of time, much has happened to the language spoken when a settlement was first established and named. Pronunciation and spelling have suffered frequent and subtle change. Words have been contracted, corrupted and distorted so that the original meaning may now be totally hidden from view. Two or more places given identical names at the time of their foundation, may now bear different names. Keswick differs from Chiswick, but both were originally the site of an outlying farm that was noted for the making of cheese. Early English settlers had a word 'bearu' which meant a grove or wood. When used in a place name it has come down to us in a variety of forms including bere, bare, or beer. Conversely, identical names on today's map may have different meanings. There is an iron bridge at Ironbridge (Shropshire) but not at

Ironbridge (Essex). The common place name Walton may have one of at least six different meanings, depending on the Old English word from which the first syllable is derived.

The origin of some place names is shrouded in mystery, but for the majority, meanings can be determined from the earliest spellings recorded in ancient documents. These, together with local history and topography, are the basis of the serious study of place names. This is the sphere of the specialist, but happily there is an extensive and helpful literature on the subject, much of it written with the general reader in mind. Dip into *The Oxford Dictionary of English Place Names*, compiled by Ekwall, and most questions will be answered.

Although meanings are seldom clear from modern spellings, there is much of interest in place names as they appear on the OS map. Some common place-name elements, especially the final ones, have not changed with time. 'Sand' and 'land' mean the same today as they did over a thousand years ago. The spelling of the Old English word 'croft', meaning a small area of enclosed farmland, has been similarly preserved. 'Holt', one of several Old English words for wood, is a further illustration. Other elements have changed in regular and consistent fashion. 'Weg', meaning road, has come down to us as 'way'. 'Waed' (ford) and 'ecg' (ridge) are now normally -wade and -edge respectively. If a settlement has a name which ends in -fleet, we can be confident that it lies on the banks of a river or estuary.

Peoples and languages

Place names add important footnotes to the unfolding story of British history. In their diversity, they contribute to the character and personality of individual map sheets. For illustration, *extract 8* (page 87) may be compared with *extract 9* (page 91). The contrasts stem mainly from the different languages spoken by the communities who first named the settlements. In early times

Britain was the target of successive waves of immigrants, and the speech of each is echoed in present-day place names.

The first influential migrations were those of the Celtic tribes who made steady inroads in the centuries before the birth of Christ. In two main groups, speaking closely related languages, they approached from different directions. One line of approach ran through Ireland and into Scotland. The other took a stream of settlers from east to west across southern Britain. The impact of their language is strong on many OS maps.

Celts were followed in the first century AD by the conquering Roman legions. For four centuries, Britain, especially the lowlands, was dominated by the power and culture of Rome, but significantly not by the Latin language.

This was not the case with the language spoken by the next wave of immigrants, the Anglo-Saxons, who made their first incursions early in the fifth century. Like the Celts, but unlike the Romans, they came in large numbers in search of new farmland. It was a time of large-scale forest clearance and settlement. Their language, today described as Old English, has made a varied impact on the OS map. The wave of settlement was strong in the east but steadily faded, and made no impact on the western highlands, which remained strongly Celtic in language and culture.

The aggressive incursions of Scandinavian peoples brought a new language to Britain. Groups from what is now Denmark crossed the North Sea and came to control and settle much of England north and east of a line from the Thames to the Dee. Scandinavian folk from further north—the Norsemen—took settlement steps around the north and west coast of Scotland to Ireland, and later to north-west England. Historical evidence is supported by place-name study. Areas of Scandinavian influence can be identified on the map, and slight differences in language enable us to distinguish between the areas occupied by Norsemen and Danes.

By 1066 the settlement map of Britain was virtually complete. The Norman invaders came as lords and masters rather than common peasants. Relatively few settlements were founded, but a new language had an influence on existing names. Spelling was often modified by French-speaking scribes unaccustomed to the local language, and some settlements received new and distinctive additions. The Normans were the last to contribute a new language to the story of British place names. Norman French slowly blended with older languages to create the English we speak today.

Welsh place names

In areas which experienced two or more waves of settlement the echoes of each may be detected on the OS map, and the pattern is often complex. In contrast, the pattern in Wales is relatively simple. Various peoples intruded upon the fringing lowlands, but none could penetrate far into the principality's mountainous heartland, where place names are still almost exclusively Celtic in origin, and readily understood by the many with a command of modern Welsh. In medieval times and later, some names, especially of larger coastal settlements, were anglicised by untutored English tongues. They have recently regained their native spelling. Conway and Portmadoc, for instance, now appear on OS maps as Conwy and Porthmadog respectively.

In the Celtic languages, adjectives follow rather than precede the nouns to which they refer. Perhaps the most common place-name element in Wales is Llan-. This originally meant an enclosure around a church, but has come to mean the church itself and its associated hamlet or village. The name of a saint, or, more rarely, a natural feature was added. Another common first element is Tre- (or Tref-), a basic name for an agricultural settlement. Many Welsh place names are purely descriptive of the local landscape. Visitors to Pwllheli and Penmaenmawr, for instance, will appreciate why these resorts were given names meaning 'salt-water anchorage' and 'great stone headland'. The meanings of some words frequently encountered in Welsh place names are given below:

aber	river mouth
afon	river
bryn	hill
coed	wood
craig	rock
dinas	fortified place
du	black
fach	little
glyn	valley
hafod	summer dwelling
heli	salt water
hendre	winter dwelling
llan	church
llyn	lake
maen	stone
mawr	great
moel	bare hill
mynydd	mountain
nant	stream, valley
pen	head, end
pont	bridge
porth	harbour
pwll	pool, anchorage
rhos	moor
rhyd	ford
tre(f)	farm, village
traeth	sands
ynys	island

A sombre evening on the Island of Skye, one of Scotland's many Western Isles where Gaelic place names abound.

Gaelic place names

Gaelic, the language of the Celtic north, has been less successful in resisting the inroads of English, but it continues to give a distinctive flavour to the OS maps which cover the western highlands and islands of Scotland. *Extracts 9 and 21* (pages 91 and 119) provide ample illustration. In other parts of Scotland Gaelic spellings have been heavily anglicised. In the list which follows, the anglicised versions of the Gaelic words are given in the right-hand column.

abhainn	river	avon
baile	farm, hamlet	bal
beag	little	beg
beinn	peak	ben
bràighe	upper slope	brae
caol	strait	kyle
carn	stones	cairn
cill	church	kil
clach	stone	clack
coille	wood	killi
dail	meadow	dal
druim	ridge	drum
dubh	black	dub
glais	stream	glass
gleann	valley	glen
imbhir	river mouth	inver
inis	island	inch
meall	bare hill	mel
monadh	mountain	mon
mór	great	more
strath	wide valley	strath
tràigh	shore	trae
uiscge	water	usk

A useful glossary of Gaelic, Welsh and Scandinavian words which appear on OS maps is available from the Ordnance Survey under the title *Place Names on Maps of Scotland and Wales*.

English place names

In England, place names have a more elaborate story to tell. Each wave of immigrants left an imprint on the map which varies from region to region. Traces remain of Celtic speech. These lie mainly in the names of natural features, especially rivers, which were adopted by later settlers.

There are several river Avons, and the name is derived from a Celtic word (Welsh *afon*) meaning water, stream or river. Similarly, river names such as Esk, Exe, Axe and Usk are derived from another Celtic word of similar meaning. Words such as these were influential, for they were often included in the names chosen for settlements founded by later communities. Celtic influence on English place names increases from east to west and is strongest in Cornwall, where the local Celtic language was in common use until relatively recent times. The Cornish map is thick with place names which include such elements as Llan- (church), Trev- or Tre- (hamlet), Pen- (headland or hill) and Traeth- (shore).

The Latin brought by Rome was the language of army, administration and aristocracy. It made little impression on the speech of the conquered common people. The Celtic language survived the Roman occupation virtually unscathed, and Latin has had no significant influence on the place names of England. In contrast, the impact of the Germanic Old English spoken by immigrant Angles and Saxons has been profound. It superseded that of the Celtic inhabitants, and came to dominate the map over the greater part of England.

The Anglo-Saxons were farming folk who came in search of new lands to cultivate, new places to live. The words they used for their farming settlements now form the commonest place-name endings. The Old English 'tun' has come down to us as -ton, and 'ham' has stayed the same. Both words were used for an agricultural settlement, today best described as a village. Less common endings such as -worth, -wych and -wick are derived from Old English words for more specialised types of settlement. To distinguish village from village, descriptive words in great variety were added as prefixes. These often referred to natural features such as hills, streams and valleys, or to agricultural produce such as crops and animals. In some cases they have changed little with time. Thus Oxton,

Eelham and Flaxton may be translated with a fair degree of confidence. More often, however, spellings have greatly changed, and meaning is less apparent.

Some prefixes describe location. Points of the compass give us Norton, Sutton, Weston and Easton (or Aston), and -ham received similar treatment. Nether (lower) and Over (higher) are other examples.

Many villages were named after their founders. Hafoc, Cycca, Walhhere, Bucgne and Wocca are samples from a long list of Anglo-Saxon personal names, now strange to the ear, which often, much distorted, form the first element in place names. Kimbolton, for instance, may be freely translated as 'Cynebald's village'. Aelfric and Leofwaru gave their names to Alfriston and Leverton respectively.

Settlements which now have names ending in -ing, or -ings, also echo their founders. Both endings come from an Old English word for a group of people, which may have the meaning of 'people', 'descendants' or 'dependants' and is associated with a personal name. This element, frequently precedes -ton or -ham. Thus Nottingham, freely translated, means 'the village of the dependants of a leader named Snot'. It was the followers of Beorma

The village of Loppington near Shrewsbury. Its name means 'the settlement of Loppa's people'.

who first lived in the village that has since grown into Birmingham.

The Anglo-Saxons encountered the works of earlier occupants of the land. Doubtless the most impressive were the stone-built Roman towns and forts. To these they applied the word 'ceaster' (originally from Latin *castrum*, fort), with a descriptive prefix, often of Celtic origin. Ceaster has changed with time to -chester (Manchester), -caster (Lancaster), -cester (Cirencester) or -eter (Exeter). For defensive earthworks, made by themselves or others, they used their word 'burh' which has come down to us in various forms, but mainly -bury and -borough. Canterbury records the site of the fort of the men of Kent.

In most cases, the early villages prospered and grew. When population expanded to levels that could not be supported by the yield from the accessible farmland, daughter settlements were established in the surrounding forests. Many place names provide evidence of this secondary settlement. The most common are the group which includes -leigh, -ley and -ly, all of which derive from the Old English word 'leah' which originally meant a clearing (for pasture) in the woods. Such a clearing would form a suitable site for a new village. Other Old English woodland terms, which give present endings such as -wood, -hurst, -den and -grove, are further evidence of the expansion of settlement.

Old English words

A selection of Old English words, and their meanings, is given below. The right-hand column gives the forms in which they commonly appear as the final element in place names. It is worth noting that these elements may also occur as the first part of a name, or even, in some cases, stand alone. Thus 'bold', meaning 'building', is the first element in Bolden, the second in Parbold, and also occurs simply as Bold. The reader is tactfully reminded of the pitfalls in interpretation mentioned above: you only have to examine the apparently identical derivatives of the Old English words for

'pasture' and 'valley' included below.
Ekwall's dictionary is again recommended
if you want to find the true meaning of a
particular English place name.

burna	stream	burn, borne
cirice	church	church
cloh	valley	clough
cot	hut, cottage	cot, cote
denn	pasture	dean, den
denu	valley	dean, den
dun	hill	down, don
fenn	marsh	fen, ven
feld	open land	field
graf	grove	grave, greave, grove
haga	hedge	haw, haugh
hyp	landing place	hithe, ith, eth
mere	lake	mer, mere
sceaga	small wood	shaw
stan	stone	stone, stan
stede	place	sted, stead
stoc	meeting place	stoke, stock
stow	meeting place	stowe, stow

The Scandinavian peoples, after decades of
raiding, pillage and rape, eventually came
to stay. The most common place-name
ending that identifies a settlement of purely
Scandinavian origin is -by, meaning
farmstead, or, more usually, village. Such
endings are particularly numerous in
Lincolnshire and lowland Yorkshire.
Scandinavian villages, like those of the
Anglo-Saxons, were distinguished by
prefixes of various types. For the majority,
personal names, or nick-names, were used.
Grim (Grimsby), Uglubaroi (Ugglebarnby),
Forni (Formby) and Sleng (Slingsby) are
examples.

The word 'by' was common to the dialects
spoken by both prongs of the Scandinavian
invasion. 'Thorpe', however, was
exclusively Danish. The word was used for
a secondary settlement thrown out from an
older village. Most places with names
ending in -thorpe have remained small to
this day. The ending -toft, 'homestead', is

Gatesgarthdale reveals in its name the former presence of viking settlers.

similarly restricted to areas of Danish influence.

The Norsemen, too, had words not shared by their fellow Scandinavians. 'Brekka', for instance, meaning hill or slope, gives place names ending in -breck or -brick. Another example is 'Gil', a deep-sided valley, which has since gained an additional 'l'. Place names which include these elements are common in north-west England. Maps of the Lake District are particularly rich in evidence of former Norse occupation, especially in the names of natural features. Tarn, beck, howe, fell, dale and scale, will be familiar sounds to the region's many regular visitors.

Seldom, however, is the OS map totally dominated by place names of Scandinavian origin. The Anglo-Saxon influence shines through in varying degrees, and -tons and -hams are found even in areas of dense Danish settlement, such as coastal

Lincolnshire. There are several reasons for this. Villages taken over by Danes often retained their Anglo-Saxon names. In other cases, the name of a new and foreign owner was substituted for an existing descriptive prefix. Thus we have Grimston as well as Grimsby. There is also the possibility that, particularly on the fringes of the occupied areas, Anglo-Saxon communities were left undisturbed.

The Normans came to take possession of villages, not to establish new ones, yet their language has had a significant effect on place names. Chapel-en-le-Frith and Ashby-de-la-Zouch speak French, at least in their middle syllables. Beaulieu, Beaumaris and Belvoir have as their first element a French word for beautiful. However, the greatest contribution made by the Normans to the settlement map lay in the creation of compound names, particularly common in southern England. The family name of the new owner was frequently added, occasionally before, but usually after, the existing village name. Leighton Buzzard, Kingston Bagpuize, Milton Keynes, Marston Maisey and Albright Hussy are charming examples. When a new church was built, the name of its patron saint was often used as a suffix to give, for example, Ottery St Mary and Sutton St James.

Chapter 4

Echoes from the past

Britain is rich in sites of archaeological and historical interest which range in age from the distant mists of the stone ages, thousands of years ago, to relatively modern times. The distribution of these sites is uneven. It reflects the varying attractions of an area at different periods of time, and the pressures, natural and human, that lead to the removal of these remains from the landscape.

They are thick on the ground in certain regions, particularly those areas composed of chalk rock which, centred on Salisbury Plain, extend in fingers of wolds and downs to the eastern and southern coasts of England. These were popular areas in earliest times. They carried thin woodland that could be cleared with simple tools and fire. Their thin, light soils were adequate for primitive forms of agriculture.

Less well blessed were the lowland vales of England, where heavier soils and dense oak forests delayed development until the coming of sharper, stronger tools and ploughs. In these areas, many sites have been lost through constant tillage and redevelopment. Remote upland areas often contain lonely but impressive sites which have well withstood the test of time and the attentions of man. Few places in Britain are far from a site of interest and importance.

One does not need to be a professional archaeologist to appreciate the remains of the past. An ancient site or monument, picked out from the map, can be an intriguing destination for the layman and his family. Stonehenge, for instance, is one of Britain's 'honeypots', attracting huge crowds. Castles, too, hold fascination—be

Ludlow Castle, Shropshire, with circular Norman chapel.

Fig. 1

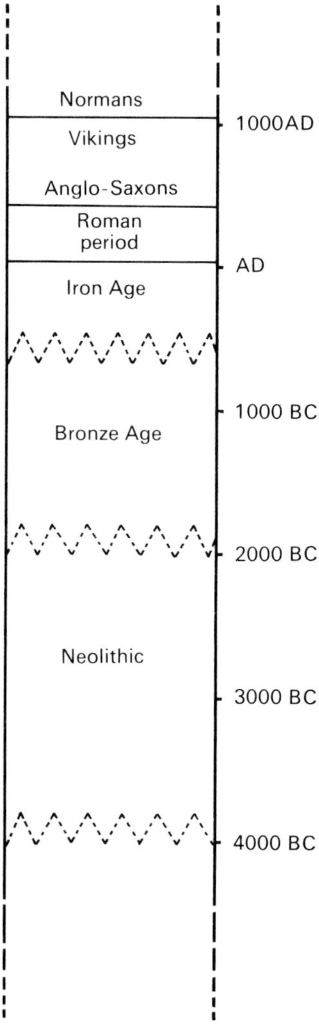

they King Edward I's majestic creations along the North Wales coast, or ones that have, through the attentions of time, weather and perhaps Oliver Cromwell, been reduced to the merest rump. Even more modest sites, today perhaps no more than a slight bump or depression on the land surface, can add interest to a country walk, especially if we know a little of their significance.

The OS map provides a remarkably detailed record of visible sites. The modest entry in the marginal key under the heading of 'antiquities' does no more than hint at the wealth of information that the map contains. The sites are mainly located by the name of the kind of antiquity, which may often be unfamiliar, rather than by symbol. The map provides few clues as to the age of a particular feature. Remains of the Roman period are named in a distinctive typeface, but antiquities of all other periods, both before and after the Romans, are labelled in 'gothic' type. The sequence of these various periods is given for reference in fig. 1. Dates are quoted, but they are general figures, for change was always slow and occurred at different times in different areas. Antiquities that may be encountered when using the OS map are briefly described below.

Burial mounds

Long barrows date from the neolithic period and are the oldest antiquities that are common and prominent in the landscape.

West Kennet long barrow, Wiltshire.

They are long mounds, slightly wider and higher at one end, and flanked by ditches, now often indistinct, on either side. They are typically 30 or 40 metres long with a maximum height of 2 metres or so. In chalk country they are composed of earth and broken rock, now grassed over into smooth slopes. Most long barrows were raised above collective burials, and excavations have revealed the remains of as many as fifty bodies. Some contained stone-built

Wayland's Smithy chambered barrow, Wiltshire.

Cairnholy, chambered cairn, Dumfries and Galloway Region.

Tumulus, Otterford, Somerset.

chambers to house the dead. Long barrows are strongly associated with the chalklands of England.

In other parts of the country, especially the highland west and north, where stone was readily available, *chambered cairns* served a similar purpose, and the chamber that received the dead was buried beneath piles of rock. In some cases, the rock has been robbed for later walls and houses, and only the stark slab outline of the chamber remains. These ancient burial mounds must not be confused with the modern cairns that mark the course of many a mountain path.

Tumuli and cists

With the bronze age came a change in burial customs. Long barrows and chambered cairns gave way to the *tumulus* (plural *tumuli*). These are the most numerous of all antiquities plotted on the OS map, and they merit their own special symbol, a five-pointed outline star. They have a variety of local names including barrow, law, toot, tump and cairn. They vary considerably in form, but the great majority appear today as a low, round, grass-covered mound, with or without a surrounding ditch. Dimensions are generally modest. A good example might have a diameter of 30 metres and a maximum height of six metres. Some, while sharing the same shape and dimensions, are in fact made of stone, and bear the name *cairn*. This increases the confusion associated with the word, but at least the use of gothic type places all these burial sites firmly in antiquity.

In some upland areas, the bronze-age dead were buried in box-shaped structures made of stone slabs. These are known as *cists*, a word which appears frequently on maps of Dartmoor, for instance.

Harold's Stones, Trellech, Gwent.

Standing stones

Standing stones raised in ancient times may have long been considered the most fascinating and mysterious of archaeological remains. They may occur alone, in lines, or, more familiarly, in a *circle*. Some of the more modest examples date back to neolithic times, but the full flowering of stone circle construction came in the bronze age. Their distribution spans the whole of Britain from Cornwall to northern Scotland. Often, circles were built

Old Oswestry hillfort, Shropshire.

on sites that were important in neolithic times. Stonehenge, the classic example, is a case in point. The purpose of these huge constructions, raised with the most primitive of tools, has always been the source of speculation. Once considered to be the temples of priestly Druids, many experts now see in them the relics of astronomical observatories which once had the capacity to predict eclipses.

Ancient fortifications

Many of the most impressive remains of former times are those associated with defence. *Hill forts* dating mainly from the iron age are a good example. They are prominent on the ground and on the map. They occupy the summit of a hill, the end of a spur, or some other site that afforded natural defensive advantages. Typically, a roughly level area, often of considerable size, is enclosed within a set of high banks with external ditches. The entrance is particularly well guarded by these defensive works, which even today, when time and weather have lowered the banks and shallowed the ditches, are of truly impressive dimensions.

The word *broch*, printed in gothic type, records the site of a fortified iron-age site that is peculiar to northern Scotland and

Dun Carloway broch, Isle of Lewis, Western Isles.

he Isles, especially Orkney and Shetland. Set in farmland, the broch had the form of a circular windowless tower with a single protected entrance. Dry stone walls some 5 metres thick enclosed a dark interior space, up to 12 metres in diameter, which probably contained timber subdivisions. Strong as they were, the 500 recorded brochs have not withstood the test of time. Today, many are merely large piles of stones. At best, the circular base may be preserved. *Duns* and *souterrains* have a similar age and distribution. The former describes a range of stone-built forts or fortified dwellings. The souterrain consists of galleries and chambers built, at least partly, below ground level.

Many of the iron-age hill forts of southern Britain fell to the invading Roman legions. As a result of four centuries of occupation, the Romans have left their own distinctive imprint on the landscape, and thus indirectly on the OS map. The most impressive remains lie on what was once a hostile frontier. The Antonine Wall can be traced from the Firth of Forth to the Firth of Clyde. The more elaborate wall of Hadrian extends 120 kilometres from the River Tyne to the Solway Firth. Hadrian's Wall was more than just a big stone wall. *Extract 6* (page 79) hints at the complexity

Hadrian's Wall, Gilsland, Cumbria.

of the defensive fortifications. The wall itself was studded with forts, mile castles and turrets, and a great ditch or *vallum* parallels the wall to the south. The well-preserved remains are too numerous and too detailed to be fully recorded on standard maps, but the Ordnance Survey publishes a special map of Hadrian's Wall at a scale of two inches to one mile. A similar map at $2\frac{1}{2}$ inches to 1 mile covers the Antonine Wall.

Roman roads and villas

Traces of Roman military works, particularly forts, are numerous in other parts of Britain. Often, they are mapped on or near the line of a Roman road. Only rarely have even short stretches of these roads been preserved. The best example, seen in the photograph, is to be found on Blackstone Edge to the north-east of Rochdale. Sometimes, a modern road picks up the straight line of its ancient

The paved and rutted surface of a Roman road as it cuts across the high Pennine moorlands to the east of Blackstone Edge.

predecessor. Elsewhere a footpath may trace a route popular with Roman soldiers and commerce. The OS map, by fine pecked lines labelled 'Roman road, course of', records the line of all authentic examples.

Bass of Inverurie (Norman motte), Aberdeen, Grampian Region.

The *villa* was a settlement feature of Roman times, generally found in the peaceful and productive parts of lowland England. Some were suburban to Roman towns, but the majority of those excavated were the headquarters of great rural estates. The largest and most prosperous, such as that at Chedworth in Gloucestershire, were equipped at least in the living quarters, with underfloor heating and mosaics.

Later fortifications

Post-Roman times have made their own distinctive contribution to landscape, and hence to map. Features named in gothic type are often as well known as Castle and Cross, Bridge and Ford, Manor and Abbey. Others may not be so familiar. *Motte* and *Motte and bailey* are examples. These refer to the new-style defensive works which appeared in numbers as the Norman conquerors imposed their grip on Saxon England. The motte was a steep-sided, flat-topped mound of earth and rock, perhaps as high as thirty metres, on which was built a timber tower. The bailey was an adjoining area defensively fenced in timber. Some of these early castles were developed and expanded in stone as the art of castle construction developed. Others were abandoned, and now only the mound, with perhaps a hint of the outline of a bailey, remains to be seen.

The word *moat* often appears on the map, but not in association with castles. This is evidence of the moated farmsteads which were a common feature of settlement in the 12th to 14th centuries, over much of central and eastern England. Typically, a farmhouse, perhaps with outbuildings, was sited within a deep square moat, which served for defence, water supply and fishpond. Well over three thousand examples have been identified. In a few the site has changed little over the centuries, but for the majority the evidence is often no more than a depression in the ground, or a section of water-filled ditch.

Agricultural features

Some features of man's use of the land are difficult to date, or extend across several periods of time. Evidence of former

Otley Hall, Suffolk, built on the site of a medieval moated farmstead.

agricultural activity often falls into this category. Over great areas evidence is obviously scanty, because of centuries of subsequent cultivation. However, in some areas once important for cultivation, but later abandoned to pasture, the OS map notes, in gothic type, the occurrence of *field systems*. These consist of the outline of former fields, usually small in size and square in shape. Traces on the ground are slight and may be missed by all but those with a keen and experienced eye. The chalklands yet again provide many examples. They may date from any period from neolithic to Roman.

The map may also bear further evidence of farming in the word *lynchet*. When patches of land were ploughed parallel to the slope, soil shifted with gravity and became slightly banked up on the downslope side to create a flight of shallow terraces, now preserved under a cover of grassland. Dating is again often uncertain. *Strip lynchets* have the same origin, but date from post-Roman times, when the typical ploughing unit was long and narrow rather than square.

One interesting area, once important for settlement and agriculture, but now the domain of grazing sheep, is the high granite

Man's double imprint on the land. On the sloping hillside, ancient strip lynchets, 'fossils' of former arable fields, are enclosed within stone-walled pastures.

Remains of a hut in Grimspound on Dartmoor. Devon.

moorlands of Devon and Cornwall, especially Dartmoor. The map locates numerous *hut circles*. These are the stone foundations of circular Bronze Age dwellings, and they are usually associated with faint traces of fields, often marked by lines of stones. They are found at heights of 400 metres or more, which is well above the present level of cultivation. The bronze-age farmer must have enjoyed weather that would be the envy of many a present-day tourist.

The typical British farming village occupies a site which has been in continuous occupation since well before the Battle of Hastings and the subsequent Norman Conquest. Not all have been so lucky, however. At various times, because of royal or monastic commands, deteriorating climate, the Black Death, or changing economic demands, villages have been abandoned by their inhabitants. The OS map locates numerous examples of these *deserted villages*. There is not a lot to see on the ground. Dwellings of wattle, daub and thatch have rotted with time, and stone has been carted away, but the imprint often remains. In many cases, it is still possible, at least in the imagination, to tread the village streets, and pick one's way between the sites of cottages.

Earthworks

The word '*earthwork*' appears frequently on many OS maps, and the position of the earthwork is defined by small black hachures. Local names, with *dyke* or *ditch*, may refer to the same type of feature. Earthworks, as in the case of hill forts, are often part and parcel of a defended site, but in addition they may be linear features of ditch and bank, often running across country for considerable distances. Linear earthworks span the centuries from Bronze Age to mediaeval times. Some were created as defensive barriers across a vulnerable line of approach, but the majority served as boundaries, often for the control of grazing cattle. The most famous linear earthwork is Offa's Dyke which runs from the North Wales coast to Chepstow, a distance of almost 200 kilometres. It was built in the eighth century to define the frontier between the Saxon kingdom of Mercia and the troublesome tribes of Wales. Today, its course is followed by a popular long-distance footpath.

Archaeological and Historical maps

The link between the Ordnance Survey and

Offa's Dyke on Llanfair Hill near Newcastle, Shropshire.

archaeology has long been strong. In addition to the wide and detailed range of material included on standard maps, the Ordnance Survey publishes a series of Archaeological and Historical maps covering various periods and places. Those of Hadrian's Wall and the Antonine Wall have already been mentioned. In addition, Roman London is portrayed at the large, detailed scale of 1 centimetre to 25 metres. Special maps at a scale of 1 inch to 10 miles give a clear picture of Britain at important periods of the past. Ancient Britain, Roman Britain and Monastic Britain are three examples.

Extract 4

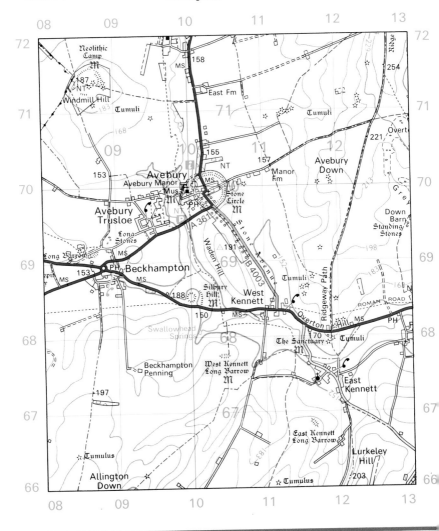

The map as a guide

The value of the OS map as a guide to Britain's ancient heritage may be appreciated by consideration of *extract 4* which is taken from Landranger sheet 173 and covers part of the Marlborough Downs. On this map one can easily plan a route to visit a wide selection of antiquities ranging in age from neolithic to Roman. Long barrows and tumuli, earthworks and field systems, track ways and stones and ditches—all are identified in gothic type. In addition, this small area, considered to have been the most populous and important area in prehistoric Britain, contains sites of particular interest.

Windmill Hill, which lies in the top left-hand corner of the extract, was the centre of close agricultural settlement in the neolithic period. It is an example of a *causewayed camp* developed between 4,000 and 5,000 years ago. It consists of three concentric rings of banks, the largest being 400 metres across. The banks, never very high, are today but faintly traced on the grass-covered surface. To the present-day visitor, Windmill Hill is not the most dramatic of monuments, but it is a site of

Avebury, Wiltshire.

great archaeological significance.

Barely two kilometres south-east of Windmill Hill lies Avebury stone circle. The site has a diameter of more than 400 metres. It is bordered by bank and ditch, which still impress with their height and depth, especially when the primitive nature of the construction tools are remembered. The remnants of a huge stone circle lie near the inner edge of the ditch, and traces of two further circles have been identified within.

The OS map shows that the old village (but not the parish church) lies in the centre of the circle, at the focus of four roads which make use of original gaps in bank and ditch. Doubtless, the needs of housebuilding made ancient stones a convenient quarry, and contributed to the deterioration of this, the largest monument of its type in the world.

Leave Avebury to the south-east by the B4003, and you follow an ancient processional way. Excavated stones have been re-erected, and the sites of missing specimens have been marked to give an impression of the ancient avenue of standing stones which linked Avebury with 'The Sanctuary'. The Sanctuary, like the

Kennet Avenue, near Avebury, Wiltshire.

Silbury Hill, Wiltshire.

whole Avebury complex, is thought to have had great religious significance in ancient times. It consisted of small circles, some of stone, more of timber posts. None remain today, but their positions have been determined by excavation and are marked on the ground.

Return to the road and travel west to Silbury Hill. This is the largest man-made mound of prehistoric Europe. Its interest is mainly in its mystery. No one knows why it was built.

Chapter 5

Fixing the spot

It is always useful, and sometimes vital, for the map user to be able to describe precisely the position of a point on the map. You may, for instance, wish to arrange a rendezvous with a friend; or, in less fortunate circumstances, you may need to call assistance. In describing your position, words can be vague, ambiguous and open to misinterpretation. Who has not waited for a friend at the right time but at the wrong place? Happily, the OS map, with its National Grid reference system, enables us to locate any point in Great Britain with absolute accuracy.

The National Grid reference system
Look at any Landranger map and you will see two sets of thin lines, blue and parallel. These divide the map into squares and form the framework of the grid reference system. One set runs from top to bottom margins, where each line is identified by a two-figure number. The lines are spaced at the map equivalent of one kilometre on the ground, i.e. two centimetres. Although their direction is north–south, they are in fact called *eastings*. This, which may be a little confusing at first, is due to the fact that they indicate distances eastwards. Note the sequence of the large marginal numbers. They always lie within the range 00 to 99, and increase from west to east. Line 99 is followed by 00, and the sequence is repeated.

The grid lines printed across the map are numbered in the left- and right-hand margins. The numbers increase northwards, and so the lines they identify are called *northings*. Again the numbers lie within the

range 00 to 99 and are repeated in sequence.
Every tenth gridline is slightly thicker.
On the most recent editions of the
Landranger series, eastings and northings
are helpfully numbered in blue on the face
of the map. It is worth noting that the
squares formed as the grid lines mesh have
an area which represents 1 square
kilometre of the ground surface.

How to find a grid reference
The use of the grid reference system may
be explained with the help of *extract 5*
which is taken from sheet 119 of the
Landranger map. It shows the small
Derbyshire market town of Ashbourne,
which lies on the southern flank of the
Peak District National Park. To the west of
the built-up area we see the familiar black
spot topped by a cross which is the symbol
for a church with a spire. This church will

Extract 5

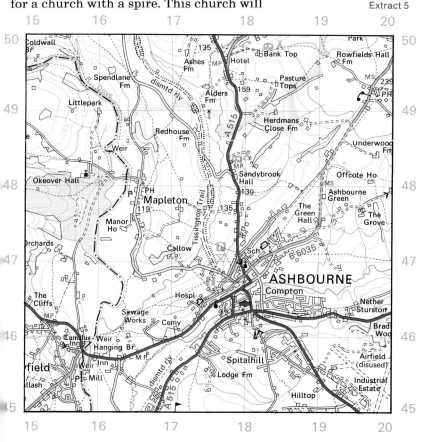

serve as an example. To find its grid reference we proceed as follows.

First, note the number of the easting to the left of the church—17. Then estimate in tenths the distance from easting 17 to the church. It is just beyond halfway towards the next easting, so six-tenths would be a reasonable estimate. 6 is the figure we need. It is quoted after 17 to give the first part of the reference, i.e. 176. Now, northings are considered. Note the number of the northing *below* the church—46. Now estimate the additional tenths northwards. This time it is just under halfway to the next northing, say four-tenths, giving the figure 4. Thus the second half of the reference is 464. The two halves are put together, eastings always before northings, to give 176 464. This is the grid reference which identifies the church.

Grid references must have six figures. Consider the bus station in Ashbourne. The distinctive red symbol lies slap on easting 18. It is *no* tenths towards the next. Zero must be included to make up the essential six figures. Its full reference is 180 464. Ashbourne also has a church with a tower. It lies at the intersection of two grid lines—easting 18 and northing 47. Its grid reference is therefore 180 470.

Small black crosses record that Ashbourne has five other churches, none of which is graced by spire or tower. They lie very close together. To distinguish their positions in words would be tedious and uncertain. With grid references they are simply and precisely identified as 177 466; 179 466; 180 464; 181 462; 182 463.

A point on the map may be identified from a given grid reference with ease and speed. Consider an example. This area has been famous for its fishing since the days of Izaak Walton. A friend in the fishing fraternity suggests a meeting at a river bridge. There are more than a dozen such bridges in the small area covered by the extract, so there might well be some confusion with a verbal description. But he quotes the grid reference 164 481. Identify the easting, 16. Picture the position of a line four tenths to its right. The bridge is on this line, and the northings will tell us exactly where on the line it lies. So picture a line one tenth beyond northing 48. The required bridge lies where the two lines cross. It is the one nearest the village of Mapleton.

The eye, with a little practice, can estimate tenths with great accuracy, but if absolute precision is needed, or if many references are required, it may be worth while to make a simple measuring device known as a *romer*. Take a piece of thin card or transparent plastic. From one corner mark off the size of the grid square and divide it into ten equal parts. Number them as indicated on the diagram. When the corner is placed on the point in need of a reference, tenths may be read off at a glance.

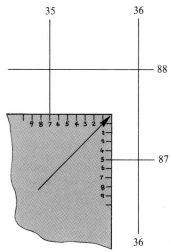

100km grid squares

It was noted earlier that grid lines, both eastings and northings, are numbered from 00 to 99, the equivalent of 100km, and that the sequence is repeated. This means that the six-figure references as given above are repeated, at intervals of 100km, over the length and breadth of Great Britain. For most purposes this is of little consequence, for even the most inexperienced map reader is unlikely to find himself 100km from where he thinks he is.

This apparent problem is solved at the cost of a couple of letters. Glance at the map overleaf, which shows the outline of the National Grid reference system. The map is squared by eastings and northings at intervals of 100km. These are the grid lines marked 00 on the individual sheets. Each 100km square is distinguished by a pair of letters. When these letters are quoted in front of a reference it is tied firmly to a particular square, and becomes unique. Every map margin contains a clear diagram which gives the appropriate letters. On the most recent editions they are also printed in the corners of the map.

Let us return to Ashbourne for a moment. The margin of sheet 119 reveals that the

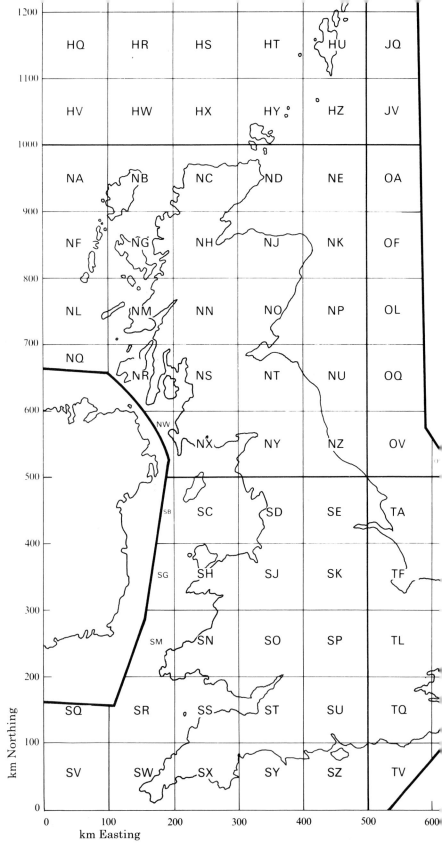

town lies within square SK. Thus the full reference of the bus station is SK 180 464. No other point in Great Britain has the same reference. It is unique.

The benefits of the grid reference system are not restricted to Landranger maps. If we look at an example of the Pathfinder series, *extract 1* (page 11) for instance, we will see the familiar pattern of eastings and northings, but here printed in black. The spacing is different because of the difference in scale. They are 4cm apart because at this scale the map needs 4cm to represent 1km on the ground. On *extract 1*, for example, there is a church at 195 169. It is worth emphasising that this church has the same reference on all OS maps which carry the National Grid Reference System, whatever their scale.

To make the use of grid references easier, the margins of all Pathfinder maps are conveniently divided into tenths. When making a romer for these maps, it must be remembered that, because of their larger scale, the divisions on the edge of the card must be twice as large (4mm) as those needed for Landranger maps.

To take advantage of the grid reference system you do not need to dress in boots and anorak. If you include the reference of your house in your letter heading, the need to give directions to visitors is unnecessary. Once your position is defined, the map itself will suggest the route. This is appreciated by a growing number of national organisations. The Youth Hostel Association, the Camping Club of Great Britain and the Automobile Association are but three examples.

Outline of the National Grid reference system.

Chapter 6

Distances and route planning

With map in hand, the distance between any two points, the length of any journey, is at your fingertips. You do, however, need to know the scale of the map before measurements can be converted into distances on the ground. As mentioned in chapter 1, scale may be expressed as a simple statement. On the Landranger map, for instance, two centimetres on the map equals one kilometre on the ground. Other map measurements have proportional equivalents. One centimetre equals half a kilometre, 4 centimetres is 2 kilometres, 7 centimetres is translated into $3\frac{1}{2}$ kilometres, and so on. On the Pathfinder map, 4cm are needed to represent 1km. Thus if a stretch of path should measure 12 centimetres on the map, division by four reveals that a walk of three kilometres is involved.

Linear scale

Happily, perhaps, distances can be obtained without the user of rulers and arithmetic. Speedy and accurate results can be obtained with the help of *linear scales*. These enable us to read off the ground equivalents of measurements made on the map, and can be found in the side or lower margins of all OS maps. The examples printed under *extract 6* are abbreviated forms of those contained in the latest second series Landranger sheets. On Pathfinder maps, linear scales differ in design but not in principle. Examples are given under *extract 12* (page 104). The map user has a choice of units. As is appropriate on a metric map, the kilometre linear scale takes pride of place. The lower scale will be

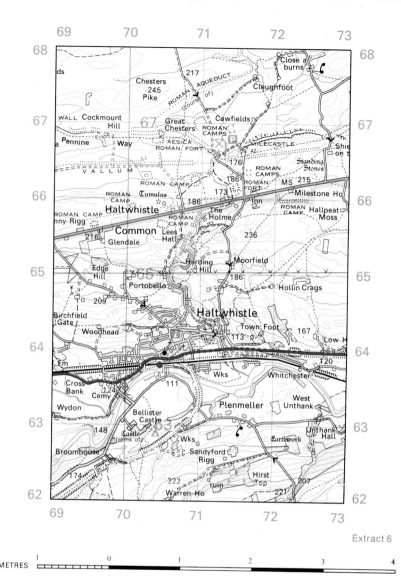

Extract 6

KILOMETRES

appreciated by the many who still find miles more meaningful than kilometres.

The use of the linear scale can be illustrated with the help of *extract 6*. This Landranger extract shows the small town of Haltwhistle which nestles in the valley of the river South Tyne between Carlisle and Newcastle. It lies just south of the Northumberland National Park and the impressive remains of Hadrian's Wall. Just north of Haltwhistle the map is crossed by a B class road. As befits a road of Roman origin it is as straight as a die. It will serve as an example. To measure its length we need pencil and paper. Place the straight edge of a piece of paper along the line of the road. Mark on the paper both ends of the road. Transfer the paper to the linear scale so that the left-hand mark is on zero. If necessary, slide the paper to the left until the right-hand mark corresponds to a kilometre division. The number of full kilometres is given to the right of zero, and tenths may be counted to the left. This stretch of road is 4.1 kilometres long. If the distance is required in miles, use the lower linear scale, which gives the distance as 2.55 miles.

Measuring distance along zig-zag or curve

Only the occasional road is as straight as the flight of a crow, and the above example must be regarded as exceptional. The Romans are responsible for relatively few of our roads. According to G.K. Chesterton, 'The rolling English drunkard made the rolling English road', and this view is supported by the course of the minor road which lurches north from the crossroads at grid reference 715 661 and crosses the course of a Roman aqueduct on its way to the top of the map. This is typical of Britain's roads, paths and tracks. They are composed of many sections which are straight or nearly so. Except on modern motorways, curves are rare, and the small bends occasionally encountered add little to total length. Such a road can best be measured by paper, pencil and linear scale.

Align the edge of the paper along the first straight section of the road and mark both ends. Then turn the paper until the edge corresponds to the second section and mark again. This process is repeated until the destination is reached. The edge of the paper now carries a series of marks. The first and last, when applied to the linear scale, will give the length of the road. It is 2.3 kilometres or, if you prefer, 1.4 miles along the road from crossroads to the top of the map.

When a route winds and curves,

measurement is less straightforward. A path that follows a large and meandering river is a case in point. On *extract 6*, the river South Tyne is not followed by a path, but a canoeist might well be interested in the length of a proposed voyage across the area shown on the map. Paper and pencil are inappropriate. An alternative is a piece of thread. With one end on the starting point, the thread is carefully arranged so that it matches every twist and turn in the course of the river. Stretched straight along the linear scale, the length of thread gives the length of the river. In this case it is approximately 5.4 kilometres (3.4 miles). This is a simple method of measurement, but manipulation of a piece of thread demands patience and nimble fingers if accurate results are to be achieved. A few small pieces of blu-tac may help.

For the measurement of distance, you can buy a variety of map measurers at modest cost. Essentially, they consist of a small wheel geared to a pointer and dial marked in kilometres and miles. When the small wheel follows a route on the map, the distance can be read from the dial. Carefully handled they give accurate results. They can be used for all measurements, but are particularly valuable when dealing with bends and curves. If you often need to measure distances they can be a good buy.

When out in the country you may find yourself without pencil, paper, thread or measurer and still wish to find a distance. In such a situation, a tall thin stem of grass can come to your aid. It is flexible enough to match gentle curves and can be bent to the course of a zig-zag path. If only a rough estimate of distance is required, use can be made of the grid squares printed on the map. The side of each is the equivalent of 1km and the diagonal is close to $1\frac{1}{2}$km. If you find miles more friendly than kilometres, the linear scales given on pages 79 and 104 serve as a ready-made conversion table.

Distance and time

To the motorist, with his close control of

speed, distance may readily be converted to time. For the walker, the challenge of distance varies greatly with circumstances. The going is quick and easy when the path is level and smooth. Progress is slow when the terrain is tough and slopes are steep. By studying the map beforehand, you can work out the nature of your route, and make a much better estimate of the time you will need.

A gentle springtime stroll can become an arduous yomp in hot and humid weather. One walks more slowly at the end of a tiring day, and the old music-hall artist was right when he sang, 'The longest mile is the last mile home'. The wise walker takes conditions and his own capabilities into close account when planning a walk. Often, when walking, conditions may change quite suddenly. Rain may fall or fog come down. Even experienced feet have been known to develop blisters. A change of route may be necessary. The map is always there to suggest shorter, safer alternatives.

Chapter 7

Direction finding

Three norths

The key to direction is north, but there are in fact three norths to be considered—magnetic, grid and true. Their relationship is indicated diagrammatically in fig. 2.

Magnetic north is the north to which a compass needle points. The difference between magnetic and true—the *magnetic variation*—is not great, but is nevertheless significant. It is not constant, but varies slightly with time and place. In 1983, in most areas of the UK, magnetic north was approximately 6 degrees west of true north, and the rate of change amounted to about 1 degree in six years. The map margins can always be consulted for precise details.

Grid north is the direction taken by the grid lines which run from the bottom to the top of the map (the eastings). The difference between these lines and true north, the

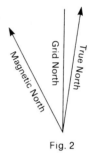

Fig. 2

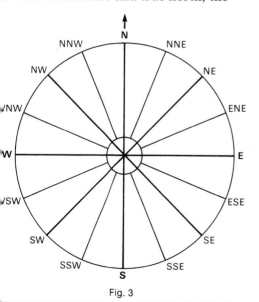

Fig. 3

direction of the earth's north pole, varies from place to place, but is always small. It is generally less than 1 degree and for most practical purposes it may be ignored. The map user is safe to regard grid north as true. Once north is known, other directions readily fall into place. Fig. 3 reminds us of the points of the compass in common use.

Direction and bearing

Extract 7 shows a handful of villages just inland from the coast of Lincolnshire, close to Skegness. Huttoft is north of Mumby. Cumberworth is south-west of Mumby, but Mumby is north-east of Cumberworth. Anderby, strung out along a road which runs from west to east, is also north-east of Cumberworth. The direction of Huttoft from Cumberworth is north-north-east. If in doubt about direction, imagine a compass diagram such as fig. 3 centred on the point from which directions are needed, and all will become clear.

Direction may also be expressed as a *bearing*. This is an angular measurement in

Extract 7

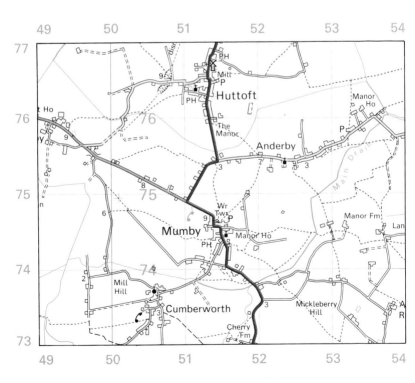

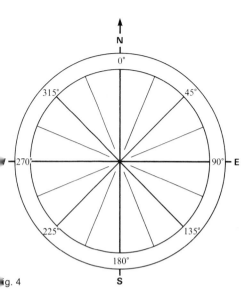

Fig. 4

...egrees, taken clockwise from north. Thus, ...s we see in fig. 4, east is 90 degrees ...lockwise from north, so it has a bearing of ...0 degrees. Similarly, south is 180 degrees ...nd north-west 315 degrees.

Grid or map bearings may be readily ...btained with the help of a protractor. If, ...n *extract 7*, a protractor is centred on the ...oad junction at grid reference (GR) 511 749, ...ith its base line parallel to the eastings, it ...ill be found that the bearing of Anderby ...hurch is 68 degrees. The bearing of Mumby ...hurch is 131 degrees. To find bearings of ...ore than 180 degrees, the protractor must ...e turned round. Angles are then taken ...lockwise from south, and 180 degrees ...dded to give the bearing. The bearing of ...umberworth church is 201 degrees. A ...ircular protractor, which marks all 360 ...egrees, is an advantage in cases such as ...his.

From the same road junction, the ...earings of the church with a tower and the ...indmill at Huttoft are 5 degrees and 11 ...egrees respectively. Clearly, the use of ...earings gives a much more precise ...easure of direction than the use of the ...oints of the compass. For the majority of ...ap users, however, such precision is ...enerally unnecessary. Bearings are mainly used in association with the compass, which is considered later.

When walking in the countryside, knowledge of north is of obvious importance. If its direction is known, your position can be checked and you can follow your route with confidence. It is seldom safe to rely on a sense of direction. This, though firmly and proudly claimed by many, often proves to be embarrassingly inaccurate. Certainly, few are as well equipped in this respect as the homing pigeon! At best, a sense of direction is a poor substitute for the certainty that the map can offer.

Setting the map

To read direction accurately, the map must always be 'set' or orientated. This simply means that the map is held so that the top of the map is facing north. The map can be set by observation. Look around and pick out two, or preferably three, prominent landmarks. They can be of any nature. Churches are obvious candidates, so too are windmills, bridges, patches of woodland, small hills and many more. Find the chosen landmarks on the map. Hold the map level and rotate it carefully until the landmarks are in line with their position as shown on the map.

When the map is correctly set, it springs into life. Landscape features fall into their proper place, and directions on the map match those on the ground. If, for instance, a correctly set map records that an orchard lies to the east of your position, a glance to the right will confirm its existence. Similarly, if you look along your left shoulder and see a village, it can be identified and named from the map.

A Suffolk example

These points may be emphasised if we let our imagination take a walk on *extract 8*, which includes a stretch of the coast of Suffolk. Drive east out of Leiston and park the car neatly at the end of the road near the Coastguard Lookout. At this starting point there will be no difficulty in setting the map. The road, the sea, and the power

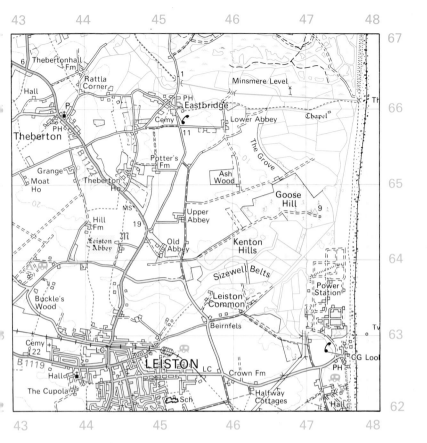

station are obvious landmarks. It may be argued that a power station is not a good starting point for a pleasant coast and country walk, and many would agree. It looks flat on the map, but doubtless it towers high to dominate the view. However, it does illustrate the point that the OS map gives a full description of the landscape, warts and all. As well as showing us the attractions it highlights features best avoided.

Nevertheless, with map set, we proceed northwards, following the right of way as far as GR 477 662, where our path is joined by one which leads west to Eastbridge. We turn—but we *don't turn the map*. Its set position—the top facing north—is retained. With the map held like this, it corresponds to the landscape and our position can be easily checked. Now, on our left, the flat land is cut by drainage ditches. On our right, a wind pump rises above the marshes. Soon, two small patches of woodland appear on our left to confirm our position.

At Eastbridge we make another left turn, but again the map is not turned. Walking south along a minor road, north is behind us and the lettering on the map is upside down. This may be a little disconcerting at first, but it is a minor inconvenience greatly outweighed by the advantages. It greatly reduces the risk of taking a turn in the wrong direction. With the map held correctly, we will not miss the bridleway that meets us on the left. This we follow, and Upper Abbey on our right, woodland first right and then left takes us to the minor road, along which we proceed. A small stream is crossed, Beirnfels left behind and at the next road junction we can turn left with confidence to return to our starting point.

The compass

Any consideration of direction must eventually lead to the compass. This simple device, though regarded with suspicion by many, can be useful on any walk, and is

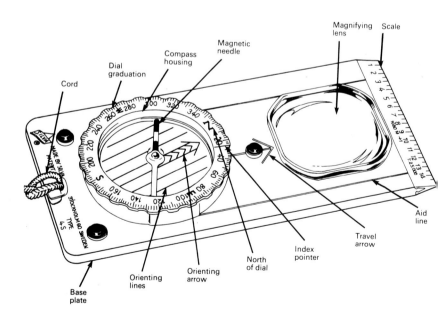

Fig. 5

essential on some. There are many types of compass on the market, all at reasonable prices. Among the most popular are those produced by the Silva company of Sweden. One of their basic models is illustrated in Fig. 5. Its rectangular base plate is transparent, so that map detail is not obscured, and includes a useful magnifying lens. Two sides serve as rulers with metric divisions, and this is handy when measuring distances, especially if used in association with the linear scale of the map. The base plate carries the compass housing, which is liquid-filled to steady the needle. The red end of the needle is the business end, the end that always points to magnetic north. The dial on the top of the compass housing can be rotated. It is calibrated in divisions of two degrees, and acts just like a protractor. Note the little white mark that is seen under the transparent dial. This is the index pointer. The parallel lines should also be noted. Those under the needle rotate with the dial. They are called *orienting lines*. The middle two are part shaded with Vs to form the *orienting arrow*. The line on the base plate that is topped by an inverted V is known as the *travel arrow*.

Such a compass has many uses, and all may be easily mastered. One point that must always be borne in mind, however, is that the needle points to magnetic north, not true north, and allowance must be made for this variation when precise readings are required. Remember, too, that the needle is attracted to anything made of iron and steel. To use a compass close to a car, for instance, will lead to the most weird of readings. Even small metal objects, belt buckles or cameras for instance, can lead to distortion.

With the help of a compass the map can be quickly set. Turn the compass dial until the index mark corresponds to zero (N). Place the compass on the map so that its long edges are parallel to the eastings on the map and the travel arrow points to the top of the map. Holding map and compass steady and level, turn them until the red end of the needle lies directly over the orienting arrow. The map is now set to a degree of accuracy that is adequate for most practical purposes. To achieve absolute precision, allowance must be made for magnetic variation. Assuming that this is 6 degrees W, map and compass together are turned until the needle points to 354 degrees (360 − 6). This method of setting a map is quicker and more useful than the visual method described above. It is effective and reliable even when cloud or mist destroy visibility, or when a landscape is devoid of suitable landmarks.

Plotting a route with the compass

Few walkers have not experienced that little quiver of alarm that comes from doubt about the path being followed. This may be felt in gentle lowland country as well as on high moorlands where paths may be hard to distinguish from the tracks made by rambling sheep. With a compass it is easy to check. Suppose, for a moment, that you are following a path which should be taking you due east. Is it? Are you in fact on the wrong path? Turn to, and trust, the compass. Hold it level in front of you so that the travel arrow is pointing along the path ahead. Let the needle settle. Turn the dial until the needle points to 354 degrees (allowing for magnetic variation). Look at the index mark under the dial, and read off the angle. If it is close to 90 degrees, you are on the right path and may proceed with a light and happy heart!

The compass enables us to plot a route and follow it with safety. This can be a useful skill in several situations, especially in the wilder higher corners of Britain's uplands. It can, in alliance with the map, free us from dependence on paths, and allow us to choose our own personal route over open country. In fog or low cloud, when all landmarks disappear, it enables us to reach our destination, or, if trouble threatens, to find a shorter, easier route to safety.

Extract 9, which covers a remote corner of the Island of Skye, provides a practical illustration. Assume that you are at the southern tip of Loch Niarsco (GR 392 467) and wish to visit, in turn, Loch a' Ghlinne Bhig and Loch Ravag. The map, by the use of contour lines (discussed on page 100), gives a detailed picture of the land surface; but even the most skilled map reader will turn to the compass, for in open country, with few clear landmarks, it is easy to wander off course. There is always the risk that mist will come down to destroy visibility, and leave you, so to speak, in the dark.

The first step is to find the grid (or map) bearing for the first leg of the walk. For this you use the compass as a protractor. Place the compass on the map so that a long edge links starting point and destination, and the travel arrow points in the direction you wish to go. Then turn the compass housing until the lines engraved on its base (the orienting lines) are parallel to the grid lines on the map and the orienting arrow points to the top of the map. Read the number of degrees indicated at the index pointer under the dial. This is the grid bearing. It is

Extract 9

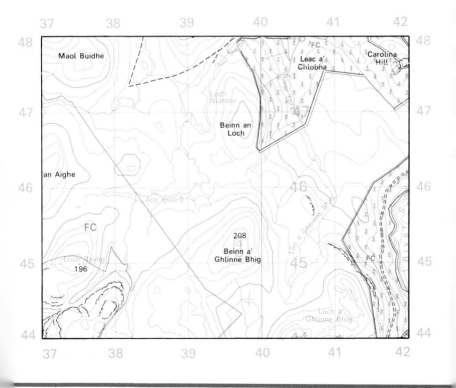

140 degrees. To convert this to the required compass (or magnetic) bearing, magnetic variation (say 6 degrees) must be added. Turn the dial through three graduations until the index pointer lies under 146 degrees. Take the compass from the map and hold it in front of you. With compass held level and steady, turn yourself slowly until you see that the red end of the compass needle lies exactly over the orienting arrow. Once this is done, the travel arrow points to Loch a' Ghlinne Bhig, and gives you the direction of your line of march.

You will not wish to walk with your eyes glued to the compass dial constantly checking that the needle and the orienting arrow coincide. It is better to pick out a feature that lies directly ahead on your lines of march, a prominent rock or an isolated bush for instance, and walk towards it. Then the procedure can be repeated until your destination is in sight.

For the second leg of the walk, you will need the compass bearing of Loch Ravag from Loch a' Ghlinne Bhig. It turns out to be 280 degrees. A third and final leg following a compass bearing of 36 degrees delivers you safely back to your starting point.

Assume, now, that on the second leg of the walk you decided to make a short detour to the summit of Beinn a' Ghlinne Bhig which is marked by the triangulation pillar at GR 397 452. While you are enjoying both the view and your sandwiches, the weather clamps down. In low cloud and driving rain, continuing to Loch Ravag is less appealing. Discretion suggests a speedy return to your starting point. A compass bearing of 350 degrees, obtained as described above, will get you there. Speaking of rain, don't forget that to carry the map in a protective plastic cover can have practical advantages.

Finding your position

The compass has still more to offer. On the homeward leg of your walk maybe you wavered and wandered, dillied and dallied,

and are now unsure of your position. Provided that you can identify two widely spaced features that can be pin-pointed on the map, the compass will enable you to fix your position with accuracy. In the small area shown on the extract, with lakes hidden in folds in the ground, suitable landmarks are few, but the summits of Beinn a' Ghlinne Bhig and Beinn an Loch will serve our purpose.

The method is known as *resection*. The first step is to take a compass bearing of the first landmark, say Beinn a' Ghlinne Bhig. To do this the compass is held level so that the travel arrow points directly to the summit. Then, without moving the compass, carefully rotate the compass housing until the red end of the needle lies exactly over the orienting arrow. Read the angle indicated over the index pointer. This is the compass bearing. It must be converted to a grid bearing so, as is always the case when working from compass to grid, magnetic variation is subtracted. Adjust the dial so that it records the grid bearing. Now place compass on map so that one long edge

The rolling heather-clad plateau of the North York Moors where paths are rare and landmarks few. Here, the wise walker will carry a compass.

passes through the summit of Beinn a' Ghlinne Bhig. Then, carefully rotate the whole compass—but not the map—until the orienting lines are parallel to the grid lines on the map, and the orienting arrow points to the top of the map. Check that the edge of the compass hasn't slipped, then use the edge of the compass as a ruler and draw a line on the map. Your position is somewhere on this line. If the process is repeated using Beinn an Loch, the two lines will cross on the map. The cross marks the spot where you are standing.

If the grid bearings obtained from the above process should happen to be 286 degrees and 246 degrees respectively your position will be near the marshy source of the small stream named Allt Dearg. From here you can follow the stream to the lake, or, and this gives a shorter route, follow a bearing worked out from the map.

Used in similar fashion, but from a known position, the compass enables you to identify a particular landscape feature. Suppose, for instance, that you have achieved a viewpoint, and a skyline with several peaks commands your attention. Which is which? Select a peak. Take its compass bearing and convert it to a grid bearing as described above. Place the compass on the map so that one edge lies on your position and the orienting lines are parallel to the grid lines. The edge of the compass now links the viewpoint and the selected peak, the name of which can be read off from the map.

The simple techniques described above can be quickly mastered at the cost of a little practice. Proficiency—soon achieved—gives you confidence in the compass, and leads you to appreciate its value. The modern compass, although small, light and cheap, is nevertheless a highly accurate instrument and is worthy of our trust.

Part III

A FEEL FOR THE LANDSCAPE

Photograph

Chapter 8

The third dimension

Photograph 2

The photograph (no. 2) which appears above was taken near Wisbech, in Cambridgeshire. A lonely, splendid tree rises proudly from the grass-covered banks of a deep drainage ditch and casts a small pale shadow on the rich cornlands which extend to the straight and distant horizon. It is a landscape typical of the flat plains of Fenland, which border The Wash in eastern England. This landscape, to which, as ever, the OS map serves as a detailed guide, has charm and interest, but it lacks a dimension clearly evident in the photograph opposite (no.1). This gives us a glimpse of the Trotternish Hills in Scotland's Island of Skye. A strip of hummocky lake-studded lowland extends to the horizon. It is flanked by higher, broken land that rises steeply to pointed peaks or high but gently sloping surfaces. The land is seen to vary greatly in height and slope.

Height and slope

It is variations in height and slope that make the major contribution to an area's scenic charm. Most would agree that the area seen in photo 1 offers more inspiring views than those in photo 2. Height and slope are also of practical significance to the map user, be he walker or cyclist. If the land is flat there is only distance to overcome. In more varied terrain he has the additional challenges of heights to achieve and slopes to conquer. The map provides a picture of both in the finest of detail.

At Newlyn on the Cornish coast, the level of the sea is recorded in all its tidal phases—high and low, spring and neap. Levels are averaged out to give the value of mean sea level, which is the base line or datum from which all measurements of height are made. On OS maps heights above sea level may be given in metres or feet, depending on the map series and the progress of metrication. On Landrangers, all heights are now given in metres, but conversion of the Pathfinder series is not as yet complete, and on a few of these maps heights are still given in feet. When using a map it is essential first to check which units are used. Details are given in the marginal key.

Height above sea level, or altitude, is determined in the normal course of survey. To represent this information—the land's third dimension—on the flat printed sheet, is a major challenge to the map maker. The area seen in photo 1, for instance, must be portrayed in such a way that the map user may readily appreciate all the subtle variations of height and slope that give the land its texture.

Spot heights

Altitude can only be represented on the map by conventional means—signs and symbols. Of these the simplest is the *spot height*. A point on the map is marked by a dot, and the height of the land is printed alongside.

On Landranger maps, spots and heights are printed in black. Pathfinders have two types—some determined by ground survey and other by precise stereoscopic measurements from overlapping pairs of aerial photographs. The colours used to distinguish these are black and orange respectively.

Spot heights are frequently found along roads, and crown the summits of many hills. If, for instance, you climb to the top of Ben Earb (*extract 21*, page 111) you will have achieved a height of exactly 801 metres above sea level.

Height is also precisely recorded at the site of a triangulation station, the symbol for which is a dot set in a small triangle, blue on Landranger, black on Pathfinder. In open country triangulation stations are pillars of concrete or stone some two metres high. They are essential reference points for the surveyor. The height recorded is, incidentally, the height of the land at the base of the pillar.

Spot heights are used sparingly, for too many would clutter the map and make it difficult to read by obscuring important detail. The main device for depicting height

Extract 10

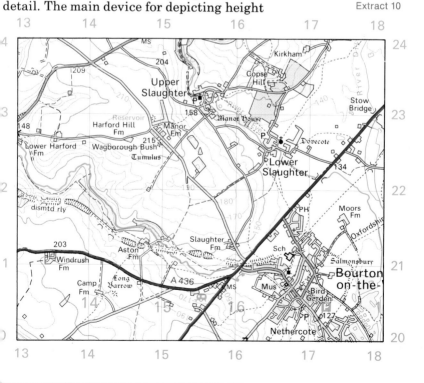

is the *contour line*. This is a line on the map which joins all points of the same altitude.

Contour lines

Extract 10 presents a delightful corner of the Cotswolds just to the east of Cheltenham. It shows contours as they appear on the fully metricated editions of the Landranger series. The orange lines twist and turn as they faithfully mirror the subtle rise and fall of the land surface. Every fifth contour is slightly thickened, and this is a useful aid in interpretation. The difference in altitude between successive contours is known as the *contour interval*. This sets the limits of accuracy to which we can determine height above sea level. On this map, the contour interval is 10 metres. Thus, with the aid of contours, we can quickly determine the height of any point on the land surface to the nearest 10 me†

Not every contour is numbered. The lucky ones carry their values (without indication of unit) in breaks in the line. A glance at the map reveals that contour values are printed at all manner of angles. They are printed in relation to the slope of the land. They always face uphill. This is an important point to remember, for it enables us to work out the values of adjacent unnumbered contours.

Extract 10 on the previous page will help to illustrate the ways in which contour lines are used to determine altitude. At GR 159 213 we identify Slaughter Farm, a name that is not too surprising in view of the villages just to the north. This farm is on a contour line. Just to the east the same contour is numbered 150, therefore we can be sure that Slaughter Farm lies at a height of 150 metres above mean sea level. Hartford Hill Farm, GR 145 227, also lies on a contour, but this must be followed a little further before its value of 210 metres can be found.

Not all heights can be so easily determined. Take Lower Hartford Farm (GR 135 227) for example. It lies on a contour line, a thicker one as it happens, but one which, within the confines of this small extract, carries no number. Follow it a short way to the north-east, however, and we find that it runs close to one that is numbered 210. From the way the figure is printed, it is clear that the thicker contour is lower than 210. The contour interval is 10 metres, therefore the value of the thicker contour, and hence the height of Lower Hartford Farm, must be 200 metres.

Consider now the buildings named Kirkham (GR 169 239). These, too, lie on a contour line, but values in the vicinity are rare. However, all is not lost, for a contour labelled 140 is found to the south. Again we note the way the number is printed. This time we must count up, in units of 10 metres. The thicker contour serves as a check, for it must be 150. We continue counting up to obtain the value of 170 metres for the height of Kirkham.

Now take the case of Moors Farm, GR 174 216. It does not lie on a contour line. Indeed, contours are rather sparse hereabouts. 140 is found to the north of Lower Slaughter, and so the one that makes a brief appearance in the extreme south-east corner of the extract must be 130. As Moors Farm does not lie on a contour line, we can't be precise about its altitude, but to describe it as being between 130 and 140 metres above sea level is accurate enough for most practical purposes.

Spot heights can often be a useful aid in identifying contours. Return to Moors Farm. There is a spot height with a value of 134 just to the north. The land between the two adjacent contours must therefore lie within the range of 130 to 140 metres. Take another example. Windrush (Farm) is found on a thicker unmarked contour at GR 135 210. From its proximity to the spot height of 203, we can fix its value as 200 metres.

A general point that may prove helpful on occasions is that within a closed contour, the land is always higher than the value of the enclosing contour.

Non-metric contour intervals
Until the lengthy process of metrication is

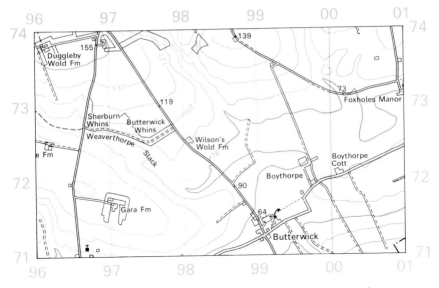

completed sometime in the 1990s, the
Ordnance Survey will continue to publish
Landranger maps with a contour interval
different from that described above. *Extract
11* is an example from Landranger sheet
101, and it depicts part of the Yorkshire
Wolds near Scarborough. Heights are given
in metres, but examination of the printed
values reveals a degree of irregularity. The
rather odd sequence of 107, 122, 137 will be
noted in the north-west corner of the map.

These maps were surveyed in imperial
units and the contour interval was 50 feet.
This, converted to metric, is 15.24 metres,
an impossibly clumsy figure to print on a
map. So contours are numbered to the
nearest metre. 15 is followed by 30, but then
by 46, and so on. This irregularity may be
considered slightly irritating, but for
practical purposes it may be ignored.
Counting in units of 15 metres gives an
acceptable level of accuracy. Take, for
instance, Wilson's Wold Farm at
GR 981 725. Counting up from the contour
labelled 76 gives the farm an altitude of 91
metres. Counting down from 107, it is 92
metres. A difference of one metre is hardly
significant.

On this extract only four contours are
numbered, yet the altitude of every point
may, within the limits set by a contour

interval of 15 metres, be determined without undue difficulty. In the north-west corner of the extract, Duggleby Wold Farm shelters within its windbreaks from the winds which may sweep across this open rolling landscape. Counting up from the numbered contour reveals that its altitude is in excess of 152 metres. No other contour is shown so its altitude is best described as being between 152 and 167 metres above sea level. Counting up from 76 in units of 15 metres reveals that the similarly protected Gara Farm (GR 970 716) has an altitude of between 121 and 136 metres.

Pathfinder contours

On maps of the Pathfinder series, there are no less than four possible contour intervals. This is less bothersome than you might fear, but before using a particular map it is essential to check, in the marginal information, which contour interval is employed. Contours are in orange and, again, every fifth one is helpfully thickened. They are used in the manner described above.

On fully metricated editions the contour interval may be 5 or 10 metres, depending on the nature of the land. Sheets covering gentle lowland areas use the 5-metre interval. Upland areas, where land is high and slopes are steep, are mapped at the larger interval.

Extract 12 on page 104 shows part of the coast of Orkney. The contour interval is 5 metres, which offers a fine degree of precision. We find that the croft of Garth (GR 232 109) has an altitude of between 110 and 115 metres. Stank (GR 233 101), however, is lower. It lies between 75 and 80 metres above the mean level of the nearby Atlantic Ocean.

This extract contains an example of an interesting arrangement of contour lines. Follow the coastline north of Alga Bar (GR 221 106), and note how the contour lines stop short at the sea. This is an indication of the presence of vertical or near vertical slopes. The value of a contour that ends in this way gives the height of the cliff. In this example, the cliffs achieve a

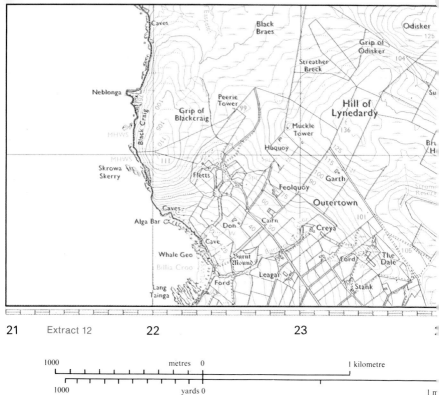

respectable maximum height of 90 metres.

Some Pathfinder maps are based on surveys made in imperial units with an interval of 25 feet. The metric equivalent of 25 feet is 7.62 metres. Contours have been re-numbered to the nearest metre, and, as with some Landranger maps, this gives an irregular sequence of values. In this case it goes 8, 15, 23, 30, 38 and so on. In using these maps, the assumption of an interval of 8 metres gives results of acceptable accuracy.

Extract 13 has been taken from a map at the Pathfinder scale which is patiently awaiting metrication. It shows Bransdale, small, isolated and neatly ringed by a minor road, which lies hidden in the depths of the North Yorkshire Moors. Every fourth contour is thickened. Heights are given in feet, and the contour interval is 25 feet. This extract well illustrates a general point that is often useful in reading the contours. Flowing water always follows the line of the lowest land, so contour values are repeated on either side of a river. Thus, we

now that the first thick contour to the east
of the river matches the one labelled 700
hat is mapped on the west. Then with our
back to the river, we can count uphill in
units of 25 feet to find that Smout House
(GR 626 976) is built on land between 825
and 850 feet above sea level.

Height on Tourist and Routemaster maps
The popular series of Tourist maps,
described on page 21, have their full
complement of spot heights and contours,
but include other methods of showing
height and relief. These vary from sheet to
sheet. Most are layer-coloured. At intervals   Extract 13

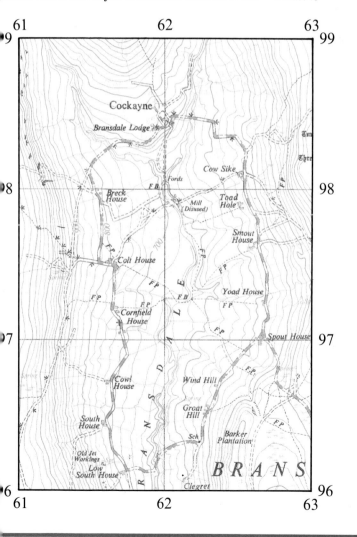

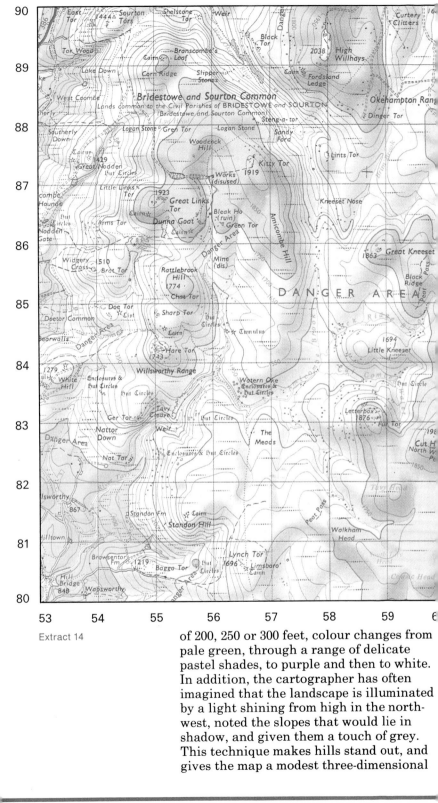

Extract 14

of 200, 250 or 300 feet, colour changes from pale green, through a range of delicate pastel shades, to purple and then to white. In addition, the cartographer has often imagined that the landscape is illuminated by a light shining from high in the north-west, noted the slopes that would lie in shadow, and given them a touch of grey. This technique makes hills stand out, and gives the map a modest three-dimensional effect. These techniques are also used with great effect on Routemaster maps.

Extract 14 is an example from the Tourist series, and shows part of the Dartmoor National Park, just south of Okehampton. It is an attractive and colourful representation of this wild and lonely corner of Devon. It gives a fine visual impression of the landscape. Colour differences, helped by the grey shading, highlight the contrasts between highland and lowland. Rolling summits stand out as purple patches. A spot of white attracts the eye to High Willhays, which, at 2038 feet, is the highest point on Dartmoor. Valleys appear as fingers of lighter tints.

Gradients

Contours do more than tell us the height of the land. They paint a clear picture of the steepness and nature of every slope. The land surface may vary through all the gradations from level to vertical, and all are reflected in the spacing of the contours. The general rule to remember is that the closer the contours, the steeper the slope. Level land, be it low or high, stands out in white because of its lack of contours. On steep slopes, contours cluster closely. For very steep or precipitous slopes, there may not be enough space on the map to accommodate all the contours that fight for inclusion, and the black rock symbol may be used instead.

Illustration is provided by *extract 15* on page 108. In this area there are marked variations in the degree of slope and each is faithfully reflected in the spacing of the contour lines. An imaginary walk can help to build up a clear and accurate picture of the lie of the land. Beinn a' Chapuill (GR 210 427) which achieves a height of 407 metres, is a convenient starting point. In this part of the beautiful Island of Skye, flat land is exceedingly rare, but immediately to the east of Beinn a' Chapuill a pair of widely spaced contours defines a small patch of land with a slope that can be no more than gentle.

The tight pattern of closed contours tells

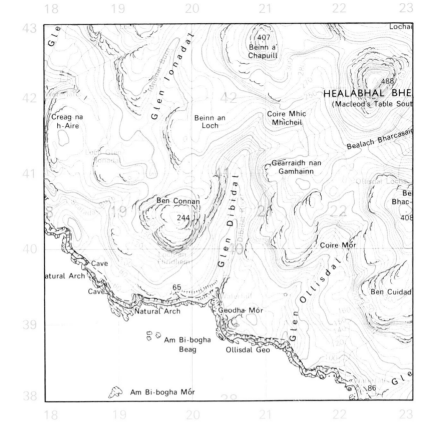

us that Beinn a' Chapuill has steep sides, and moving to the south-west we must descend sharply to 330 metres before we meet more modest slopes. It is a brief respite, for soon the contours close up to indicate a short steep drop from 300 to 250 metres. Continuing south-west and downhill across Beinn an Loch, contour spacing, though irregular, is generally wider and slopes are therefore more moderate. A short steep climb takes us to the top of Ben Connan. This summit, like our starting point, is framed by closed circular contours. Here, however, the inner rings are more widely spaced, indicating that Ben Connan is more rounded, less sharp than Beinn a' Chapuill. After a welcome pause to admire the view we are left with the problem of our route to the coast. Except to the north the contours between 150 and 200 are so tightly jammed ogether that they are hard to distinguish. his precipitous, rocky slope must be egotiated, if a lengthy detour is to be voided.

Calculating a gradient

Thus, with a little practice, the relative steepness of slopes indicated on the map may readily be assessed by eye. If a precise measure of steepness is required, the gradient may be obtained from the map at the cost of a simple calculation. Gradient is the relationship between distance travelled and the height gained on the journey.

Divide the former by the latter and you have a figure for the gradient. Both measurements must be expressed in the same units. If, for instance, on a walk of a 000 metres (1 kilometre) you gained 200 metres in altitude, the slope you climbed has a gradient of 1 in 5 (or 20%). If the distance travelled had been twice as great for the same gain in altitude, the gradient would have been a more manageable 1 in 10 (10%). The impetuous may charge straight up a slope of 1 in 5 and be rewarded by a sense of achievement and loss of breath. The more thoughtful walker will zig-zag his way to the top, for by increasing the distance travelled he reduces the gradient

Variations in the steepness of slope, recorded on the map by means of contour lines, contribute to the scenic beauty of this part of the North York Moors National Park.

to less demanding dimensions.

For road users, the Landranger maps indicate steep and troublesome gradients by special symbol. A double arrowhead in black indicates a gradient of at least 1 in 5. A single arrowhead covers gradients between 1 in 5 and 1 in 7. In both cases, the arrowheads point downhill.

Types of slope

A slope of constant gradient has contours equally spaced and is described as regular or uniform. Long regular slopes are relatively rare, for landscape is infinitely varied. Within this variety it is possible to recognise other types of slope which are worthy of note.

Extract 16

Imagine a walk on *extract 16* from Flear Farm, GR 766 465, north-north-east towards the south Devon village of East Allington. Initially the slope is steep, but as height is gained the contours become progressively more widely spaced and so the slope becomes more gentle. This is described as a *convex slope*. When walking in open upland country, this type of slope can be most frustrating, for your destination remains hidden until shortly before arrival.

Another imaginary walk, much tougher this time, will illustrate a *concave slope*. The

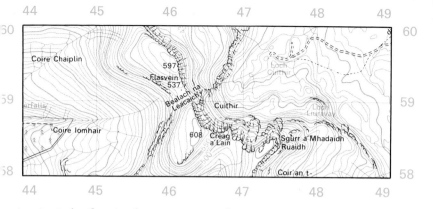

route starts in the north-east corner of
Extract 17 and takes us—if we can take
it—to the summit of 608 metres at
GR 464 586. Initially the going is reasonably
good, for the land, though rough, is only
moderately steep. Beyond Loch Cuithir,
however, the angle of slope increases
progressively, and the last lap is a
challenging rocky scramble. On a concave
slope the crest is visible throughout, but to
the walker slowed down by steadily
increasing steepness it often seems a long
time coming.

When contours are alternatively tightly
bunched and more widely spaced, the slope
may be described as *stepped*. Your descent
from Beinn a' Chapuill (page 108) merits
this description.

Valleys

Contours have yet more to reveal. Often

The crest of a dry-stone
wall mirrors the changing
slope of the valley side.

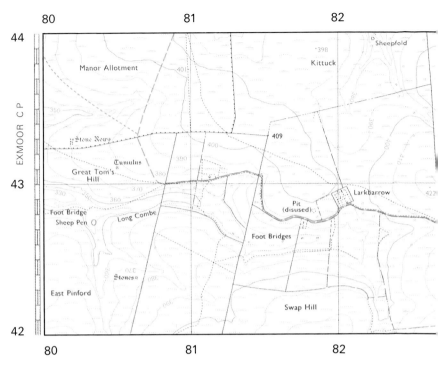

Extract 18

they are grouped into patterns which identify distinctive features of the landscape. Of these, the *valley* is the most important. As portrayed by contours, all valleys share the characteristic features that can be identified in *extract 18*, which covers a small part of Exmoor. Contour lines of equal value are roughly parallel, but eventually they meet upstream in a 'V'. Lower values are set within higher so the lowest land lies in the centre. It is here that the river flows, and it cuts each contour at

An autumn valley cuts deeply into the southern flanks of Kinder Scout, north Derbyshire.

Symonds Yat, a beautiful part of the attractive valley of the River Wye.

he point of the 'V'. The gradient of the
river's course is indicated by the spacing of
he 'V's. In a tumbling mountain torrent
hey are close together, but where a river
lows sluggishly over a gentle sloping
urface, the 'V's may be kilometres apart.

Valleys show great diversity. No two
valleys are the same and each will vary
hroughout its length from upland source to
he sea. They differ in depth, in width, in
he steepness of their sides and the width of
heir floors. They may be straight or
winding. Contours faithfully reflect these
variations in the finest details, and with a
ittle patient map reading, the map user
may readily paint a mental picture of a
particular valley.

Extract 19 on the next page hints at the

variety of valley form which contributes so much to scenery. It is taken from the first series Landranger sheet 98, which covers much of the Yorkshire Dales National Park. The river Wharfe flows from north-west to south-east. Above Hubberholme (GR 925 783), contours creep close to the river, so there is little flat land on the valley floor. The sides rise steep and high, but we detect from the spacing of the contours that the southerly slopes are slightly steeper. Below Hubberholme it is like a different valley. The contours of lowest value are far apart, so revealing that the Wharfe meanders over a wide, level floor. The straight valley sides, enlivened by strips of woodland, rise very steeply at first but then more gently to heights of more than 350 metres above the valley floor. Further contrast is provided by the valleys of Buckden Beck and Cam Gill Beck—deep

Extract 19

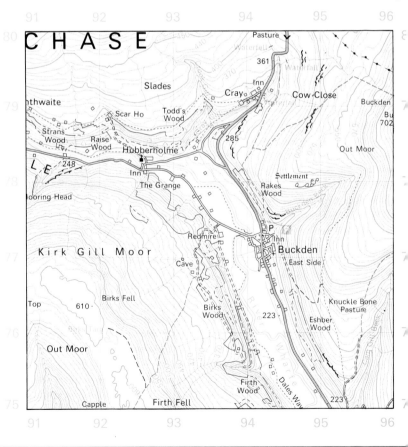

short gashes which carry tributary waters to join the Wharfe. Note, too, the tributary streams which join from the west. Only rarely do they have the power to kink the contours into the pattern which identifies a valley.

Valleys make a major contribution to landscapes of natural beauty. Often they bear regional names. It is glens that open up the grandeur of the Scottish Highlands. The Pennines are sharply cut by dales and cloughs. The dry valleys of the rolling English downlands carry the names of coombe or bottom. All offer attractive and varied scenery sheltered from the worst that the British weather can offer. If large enough to carry roads, they offer easy routes for the motorist and cyclist. Away from the roads, the walker may also appreciate the gentle gradients of path and track. To all, the valley offers a line of access to the higher, quieter land that often lies above and beyond its shoulder.

Spurs

There are a handful of other features, each with its distinctive contour pattern, which, although less important than valleys, often make a contribution to scenery. The *spur* is an example. Spurs, like valleys, vary greatly in form, but in all cases the contours double back on themselves and the highest land is in the middle. *Extract 20* on page 116, taken from the 1:25 000 Outdoor Leisure Map of the Lake District, includes a high steep-sided example. The footpath which links High Pike and Low Pike, and eventually leads south into Ambleside, follows the crest of the spur, from which the view (except to the north) is down over lower land. This spur, like most, occupies the rising land between two valleys.

Spurs and valleys have similar contour patterns, and this may be the source of some confusion. The key is the height of the land within the contours. If the highest land is in the centre, it is a spur. With the lowest land enclosed, a valley is indicated. The presence of a river is a sure sign of a valley, but care is needed, for not all valleys contain flowing water and identification

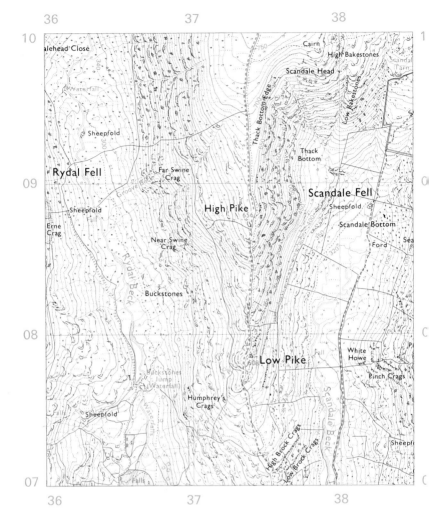

poses problems in dry areas such as the downlands. To distinguish spur from valley in the southern part of *extract 27* (page 145) is a challenging test.

Other features

A *knoll* is defined as a small isolated hill, usually rising from low, level land. Contours are closed and concentric, and the highest value is in the centre. When a similar contour pattern is found in an area of highland, it represents a peak. Many examples can be identified in *extract·9* (page 91).

A *ridge* is long and relatively narrow, and

has sides of roughly equal steepness. In highland areas they are often high, narrow and steeply sloping. They offer fine, high walking with commanding views. Typical examples are seen in *extract 23* (page 133) as they radiate from the summit of Snowdon.

Lower land within upland areas may be designated a *pass* or a *col*. The difference is one of degree. The pass is the more pronounced, and often enables an important road to pierce a mountain barrier. The Pass of Llanberis (*extract 23*, page 133) is a fine example. The col is a more elevated feature. It generally lies between two peaks and rarely carries more than a footpath. The same extract shows an example at GR 605 520.

Plain and *vale* are lowland terms. The former describes a large expanse of land of low elevation. Flat perhaps, but more usually gently undulating. A vale relates to a more restricted area, long, but relatively narrow in width, and gripped between two lines of upland.

Chapter 9

Views and vistas

Within the rich variety of Britain's scenery, certain points have special merit in that they command wide and attractive views. These viewpoints are so numerous that the Ordnance Survey can do no more than indicate, by symbol, just a handful of the more dramatic examples. Usually these are of easy access in that they lie on or near a road. Often they command the wide sweep of a major valley and the rising land beyond. The appeal and beauty of any viewpoint lies in the eye of the beholder. We can all recall, and picture in our mind's eye, the ones that have impressed us most.

To the walker, the summit of every peak, the brow of any hill, the end of every spur can claim the status of viewpoint. They are points to achieve, to pause and to ponder. The view is fair reward for the effort involved. Often a view is more deeply appreciated if its component features can be identified and named. This can be done with the help of the map.

Intervisibility

Ben Earb is a prominent peak on the southern edge of the Scottish Highlands to the north-west of Dundee. It can be found on *extract 21* at GR 079 691. With a height of 801 metres and steeply sloping sides, it has all the qualities of a good viewpoint. The map reveals that a trio of other peaks, with the impressive gaelic names of Meall a' Choire Bhuidhe, Meall Ruigh Mór Thearlaich and Carn Dearg, lies to the north-west. If, on a clear day, a hefty hike takes us to the summit of Ben Earb, will they, in fact, be visible? The height of the land is the key. Two points will not be

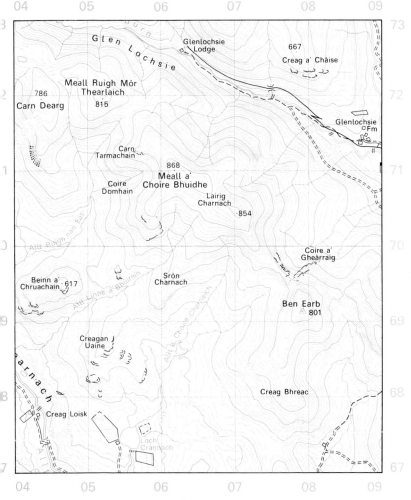

Extract 21

ntervisible (visible from each other) if
igher land intervenes. Between Ben Earb
und Meall Ruigh Mór Thearlaich the land
ises to 868 metres, which is higher than
ooth viewpoint and object. Thus, from Ben
Earb, Meall Ruigh Mór Thearlaich lies
idden from view behind Meall a' Choire
Bhuidhe. In this example, a convenient spot
leight gives a quick and easy answer.
Jsually, the contours must be closely
considered. Carn Dearg, for instance, is
nasked by the spur, 830 metres or more in
leight, which projects south-west from the
ummit of Meall a' Choire Bhuidhe.

Other cases are less straightforward. The
nap reveals a small patch of woodland

(GR 057 672) to the south of Loch Crannach. Is this woodland visible from the summit of Beinn a' Chruachain (GR 046 695)? Examination of the contours reveals that the summit height of 617 metres is not exceeded, but that the rocky spur of Creagan Uaine is considerably higher than the woodland. Is this spur high enough to obscure the view of the woodland? Pencil, paper and ruler are needed to find the answer, which is to be seen in fig. 6.

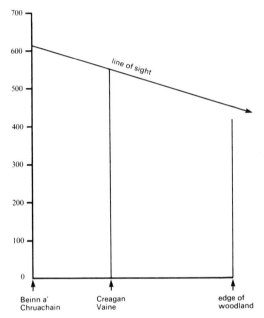

Fig. 6

The base line is the map distance from Beinn a' Chruachain to the most southerly point of the woodland. At the left-hand end a vertical line carries a convenient scale. Here, one centimetre equals one hundred metres of altitude. In areas where relief is not so pronounced, a larger scale will be more suitable. The height of Beinn a' Chruachain is marked on the scale. A vertical line is drawn at the right-hand end of the base line to represent the height of the edge of the woodland. A third vertical line, this time to the height of Creagan Uaine, is inserted at the appropriate distance from Beinn a' Chruachain. The

line of sight is seen to pass clear above the woodland, which is therefore not to be seen from Beinn a' Chruachain. Loch Crannach also lies within the 'dead ground' created by the spur.

A mountain summit is not, of course, a convenient spot to draw diagrams, even when the weather is dry and the air is still. However, a little preparatory study before you venture out will tell you what to anticipate. From Ben Earb, for instance, you can expect to see the summits of Meall a' Choire Bhuidhe and Beinn a' Chruachain. The settlement near Glenlochsie Farm (GR 087 714) should also be visible. To the south-west, Loch Crannach, but not the river, will be within your field of view.

The view from Ben Earb will, of course, extend far beyond the confines of the small area shown in the extract. From many highland viewpoints the distant skyline is crowded with summits that plead for recognition. The photograph above is typical, and with views such as this identification of individual peaks will demand the precision of compass bearings as explained on page 85.

Chapter 10

Landscape and scenery

Great Britain is three most beautiful countries. Nowhere in the world is such a variety of attractive landscapes packed into such a small area. Scotland's majestic peaks rise steeply from glen and loch. The deep clefts of the Yorkshire Dales are set in a frame of open rolling moorlands. The grandeur of Snowdonia is fringed to north and west by a coastline of wide beaches and rocky headlands. The nature of all is reflected in the twist and turn of the contour line. To read the contours is to picture the landscape.

Appreciation is heightened by understanding. Scenery is the result of natural sculpture. A long and eventful geological history has left a varied legacy of rock on which natural processes have chiselled away throughout the vast aeons of geological time. The results of this long and effective sculpture are recorded in detail on the OS map.

Rock

Natural chisels have a variety of raw materials on which to work. Rock is extremely varied. It varies, for instance, in age. On the island of Lewis, off the north-west coast of Scotland, there is an outcrop of rock that is known to be over 2,500 million years old. Over much of lowland Britain, the surface layers are formed from debris left in the wake of retreating ice sheets less than a million years ago. In an estuary choked with banks of sand and mud we see the next generation of rocks in the course of formation.

Rocks have been formed in different ways. In the granite of Dartmoor we have evidence of a huge mass of once hot and molten material which, in distant times, was intruded into the crust of the earth. There it slowly cooled into a mosaic of crystals of differing size, shape and colour. At several periods of the earth's history, huge volcanoes spewed out masses of ash and lava which have hardened into the bare bones of such attractive areas as Snowdonia and Borrowdale.

Many rocks have had a quieter, more gentle origin. These are the sedimentary rocks. Debris from the breakdown of older rocks has been sorted by size, brought together and, with the passage of time, cemented into rock. Many were formed on the floors of long-departed seas, later to be raised into land by the powerful forces active within the earth's crust. Common clay, for example, consists of particles too small to be seen by the naked eye. Sandstone is much coarser, and coarser still are the gritstones such as those once used for millstones. In the clear, warm waters of antique oceans, calcium carbonate accumulated, either as a result of chemical processes, or by the compaction of the remains of an abundant marine life. Hardened into rock, and uplifted by crustal movements, it gives the present-day outcrops of limestone and chalk. Some sedimentaries were formed on land. The red rocks of the English midlands, for instance, are made up of the small rounded grains of sand that were once buffeted by winds which blew across the surface of an arid desert.

Some rocks have been completely changed by the intense heat and pressure that may occur within the tough crust of the earth. They are known to geologists as metamorphic rocks. Muds and volcanic ash for instance, have been converted into slates of differing hues. In north Wales, the OS map records the huge bites taken out of the hillsides in the quest for roofing material. Slate gave way to clay-based tiles, and the industry died, to be remembered today mainly as a tourist attraction.

Upper Corris, a slate-miners' village near Tal-y-llyn, Gwynedd.

Fossils

It is in sedimentary rock that we must look for echoes of ancient life on earth. Remains were swamped in accumulating sediments, to be preserved as fossils. Limestones, for instance, are locally rich in shells and corals, often beautifully preserved. Leaves which fell from the trees many millions of years ago have left their fine, detailed imprint in rocks of the appropriate age. The footprints of long dead dinosaurs are cast in ancient lake-side muds. Many of us find fascination in the hunt for fossils. Beaches and cliffs, and abandoned quarries, in areas of sedimentary rock, are suitable sites for search.

Colour

Rocks also vary in colour. Many are dark and drab, even when lit by shafts of sunlight. Limestone adds a touch of light grey and reddish soils often reflect the colour of the desert rocks from which they are derived. The stark white of chalk is an outstanding colour. White rock is exposed when the thin turf and soil is removed. This

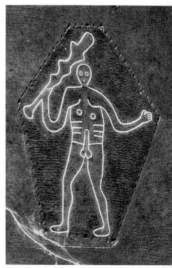

Birling Gap, East Sussex.

has been done to give the white horses and human outlines, occasionally of prehistoric origin, that shine out from the steeply sloping edges of southern downlands. Chalk is also the white of the White Cliffs of Dover.

Hardness

In terms of earth sculpture it is variation in hardness that is of the greatest significance. Some rocks are tougher than the toughest old boots, and strongly resist the natural processes that aim to carve and shape them. Others are soft and weak, and crumble to the touch. Generally it is the strongest rocks that form the harsh, sharp outlines of mountain scenery. Their weaker colleagues floor the plains and vales of the lowlands.

Thus, earth sculpture works on a variety of raw material. On rocks old and new, strong and weak, natural processes are constantly active. They work slowly and patiently. Change is usually imperceptible, but in the living landscape we can see the tell-tale signs of their activity. Such is the vastness of geological time that even the slowest process can make a recognisable impact.

A limestone hillside in North Wales is under attack by natural processes. The toughest layers of rock are more resistant, and stand out as steep breaks in the slope.

Weathering

Solid rock can be broken down merely by exposure to rain, wind, frost, and water circulating beneath the soil. In time, even the most resistant rock will succumb to the numerous chemical and physical processes collectively known as *weathering*. We recognise its work in the flaking gravestones in an old churchyard. Houses need repointing as weak mortar is weathered away from between the tougher bricks. Crack open a pebble from the bed of a stream and the unaltered core contrasts with the stained and weakened outer layers.

On a level land surface, fragments of rock will stay in place. On a slope, a valley side for instance, the products of weathering, lubricated by water and pulled by the force of gravity, are on the move. This may cause a sudden landslide, the scar of which may be visible on ground and map. More usually, the movement is too slow to be witnessed and we must look for clues. Soil banked up on the upslope side of trees and walls; telegraph poles that are less than vertical; hillsides lined with a series of tiny edges; all these signs point to the slow downhill slippage of weathered rock, which in time reduces the angle of the slope.

The fabric of Whitby parish church displays the subtle scars of weathering.

This valley side shows the tell-tale signs of soil slowly on the move.

Eventually, material is carried away to the sea by a convenient and co-operative river.

The work of rivers

The river, working on weather-weakened rock, is nature's most important chisel. Rivers have flowed since the first rains fell, and their effect is everywhere. They are patient and persistent. As we follow an upland stream all may seem placid and peaceful. The water bubbles over and around a bedload of rounded pebbles and boulders. Nothing seems to be happening, but the stream is hard at work eroding away the rock over which it flows, and steadily lowering the valley floor. Visit the valley in time of flood, and the scene is

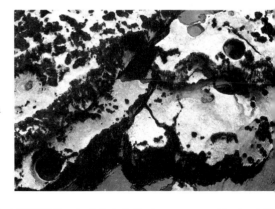

The bed of a mountain stream, and evidence of erosion, are revealed in a photograph taken when the flow was low. The tough rock is pitted by neat circular holes which were drilled by passing pebbles spun round by swirling waters.

ore dramatic. Even large boulders are
umping and banging over the river bed,
oing destructive work. Rivers work
ardest when they are roused into torrents.

The steepness of valley sides, so clearly
napped in contours, reflects the balance
etween downcutting by the river, and the
wasting away of the slopes. Active
owncutting with little wasting gives
teep-sided valleys. Where slopes are gentle,
wasting is the more effective process. On
ccasions, and for a variety of reasons,
owncutting may be of paramount
mportance. The result is a valley with
recipitous sides known as a gorge.

Often, a river flows over bands of rock
which differ in resistance. The weaker rock
s whittled away while a higher, tougher
tratum stands firm to form the lip of a
waterfall. Many of the waterfalls that
unctuate the courses of mountain streams
re formed in this way.

Meanders

n *extract 22* on page 130 we see another
spect of the river at work. A large river
wists and loops in a series of wide
neanders. This river has cut down as far as
t can go, and now its teeth are in the
astest current that follows the outside of

Under a low-hung sky, a
small upland stream
tumbles over bands of
tough rock that have
resisted its erosive work.

Tough limestone resting
on weaker slates gives
rise to the attractive
Thornton Force waterfall,
near Ingleton, north
Yorkshire.

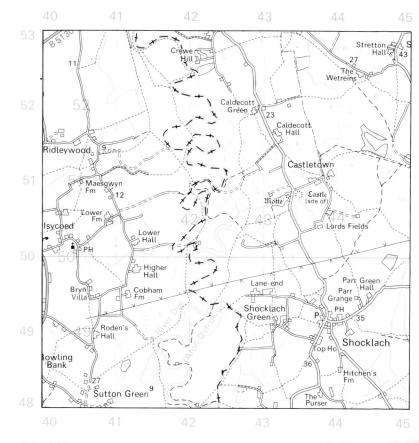

Extract 22

The level flood-plain of the River Lune above Lancaster. The small lake (bottom left) is an ox-bow, part of the river channel that has been short-circuited, sealed and abandoned.

each bend. This current nibbles away at the bank, undercutting and causing collapse. Thus, the course of the river slowly shifts outwards and the valley floor is made wider. By this process of lateral erosion wide floodplains are created. Their level surface is reflected in a lack of contours. Flat, ill drained and liable to flood, they are

generally shunned by settlement, which clings instead to the higher land along the banks.

Cuckmere River near Seaford, East Sussex.

Meanders have other tricks up their sleeves. As they expand on their outer edge, their inner arms come closer together, eventually to join up, to take the whole flow of the river. The meander is cut off, sealed off, and left as a peculiar curvaceous lake graced by the unlikely name of *ox-bow*. Thus does the river shift and shunt over its flood plain. The boundaries of administrative units, fixed long ago on a meandering river, seldom coincide with its present course. In *extract 22*, for example, we can see where the snake-like Dee has shed the national boundary like an unwanted skin.

The river does not flow empty-handed. It carries its load of weathered and eroded rock particles to choke the estuaries and

A highland tarn is shallowed and new land is created as a mountain stream loaded with debris flows in from the right.

shallow the seas. Sometimes a lake gets in the way and receives the debris. The flat land at the head of a lake is evidence of the constructive work of rivers. Soon, on the geological time-scale, the lake will be no more. A lake is always a transient landscape feature.

Ice sculpture

Rivers have not always had things their own way. At intervals over the last million years or so, the earth's atmosphere has cooled slightly to allow heavier winter snows to accumulate, be compacted into ice, and persist throughout the cooler summers. Permanent ice equipped nature with sharper chisels and heavier mallets with which to carve rocks into scenery. The effect has been profound. The beauty of Britain's mountains—the Highlands of Scotland, the exquisite Lake District, and north and central Wales—owes much to the destructive work of ice. The imprint is fine and sharp, for ice sculpture is a recent event. It was less than 10,000 years ago, less than yesterday in geological terms, that the last patches of permanent ice slowly faded away.

Through the patterns formed by contour lines, we can identify the footprints left by ice. It stamped all over the area shown in

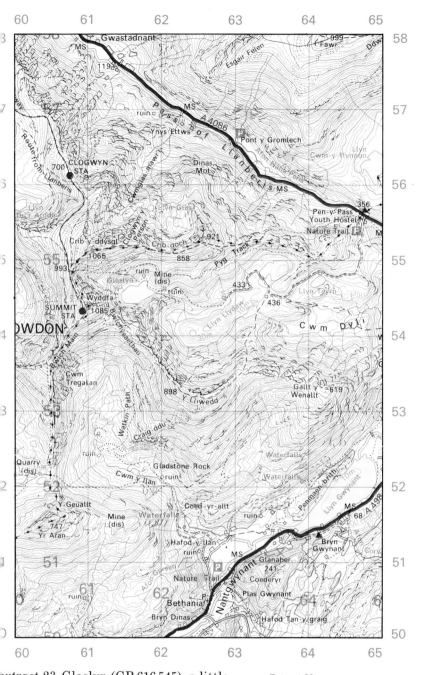

Extract 23. Glaslyn (GR 616 545), a little jewel of a mountain lake, is a good starting point. Before the ice age came, its site was merely a shallow sheltered hollow on the eastern flanks of the upland mass that has

Extract 23

since been carved into Snowdon. Snow accumulated in the hollow and, shaded from the sun, persisted in increasing depth Ice, and summer melt-water, weathered the rock and removed the debris. The depth of the hollow increased until it was large enough to hold a glacier, a slowly moving stream of thick, solid ice that staggered away to the east. The once shallow hollow was greatly enlarged as moving ice pulled lumps out of the back and the sides, and scraped away the floor. Today, with the ice departed, it is as seen in the contours—a dramatic natural amphitheatre. The back and side walls are rocky, high and very steep. The placid lake Glaslyn occupies the hollow floor.

Glaslyn is by no means unique. It is but one of many such features which scar the higher upland masses, though not all are

Llyn Idwal occupies the floor of an ice-gouged cwm in Snowdonia.

Black Cuillin Hills, Isle of Skye—looking into Coruisk, a glaciated basin.

floored by pretty lakes or tarns. In Wales they carry the name *cwm*; Scotland calls them *corries*. They often occur in clusters, especially on north- and east-facing slopes. When the wall of one cwm backs onto that of another, the result is a high narrow ridge with precipitous sides known as an *arête*. These provide exciting high-level walks with fine views on either hand. Examples can be identified on *extract 23*. The famous Snowdon Horseshoe takes the fell walker from Pen-y-Pass (GR 647 556) to the summit and back, via the arêtes of Crib Goch and Y Lliwedd.

In a sense, cwms and corries were the powerhouses of mountain glaciation. They served as collecting grounds for ice and delivered major contributions to the huge glaciers that occupied the main valleys of the area. These glaciers transformed the gentle, winding, pre-glacial valleys into the massive troughs that we see today. *Extract 23* contains examples in Nantgwynant and the Pass of Llanberis. Many close-packed contours speak of the great depth and steeply towering sides which are characteristic features of the valley which has suffered the powerful and destructive attention of a large glacier. These valleys are typically straight, for inflexible masses of ice could not adapt to the minor twists and turns of a normal valley. Ice over-rode any protruding spurs and steadily ground them away. Major glaciers bit more deeply into the rock than the smaller ones which delivered the ice. Thus, after the ice age, minor valleys may lie well above their masters. Often a tributary stream must now negotiate a waterfall or rapids before it can join the main stream. These waterfalls add attractive detail to the scenery.

On valley floors, ice erosion was locally more successful, and it hollowed out the long narrow basins which today are occupied by lakes such as Llyn Gwynant (GR 645 520). This, incidentally, is a relatively shallow example. The interval used for the blue submarine contours is 10 metres, so its greatest depth must be less than 20 metres, which is modest by glacial standards.

On a walk in a landscape of mountain glaciation, we often see evidence of the work of ice that is too small to show up on the OS map. Bare outcrops of tough rock have been rounded and polished by passing ice. Scratches, still clear and fresh, made by

Hummocky moraines on both shores of Llyn Idwal, North Wales, date from the last flicker of ice activity.

ice-gripped rocks may be identified. Moraines, short low ridges of debris dumped by waning glaciers, may lie across the valley.

It is the highest lands that display the full majesty of glaciated scenery. Elsewhere the bite of ice has been less profound, but is often to be noted in valleys deeper and straighter than normal. Yorkshire's Wharfedale (*extract 19*, page 114) is an example.

Lowland plains, as far south as the line of the River Thames, also felt the weight of ice, but not in erosive mood. Instead, much of the land was covered by thick blankets of deposits, the ultimate resting place for the masses of rock material scoured from the uplands. The former landscape was buried beneath layers of ice-borne material, often sands, more usually a heavy clay studded with ice-worn pebbles and boulders. This *boulder clay* may today give a smooth and level surface or be puckered up into gentle undulations. Occasionally, the clay has been moulded by moving ice into clusters of

This huge boulder of dark gritstone was plucked up and carried away by a passing glacier. When the glacier melted the boulder was laid to rest, several miles from home, on a surface of contrasting rock.

low, oval, streamlined hills known as *drumlins*. In *extract 24* the Leeds and Liverpool Canal snakes its way through a typical swarm of drumlins near Skipton in North Yorkshire.

Coastal scenery

At the coast, where land meets sea, it is pounding waves that are the main tool of natural sculpture. They are a powerful erosive force, especially when fuelled by strong winds which have enjoyed a long uninterrupted journey over the ocean. Wave attack is highly selective. The slightest sign of weakness is seized upon for

A low sun shadows the steeper ends of drumlins in the valley of the River Ribble.

Extract 24

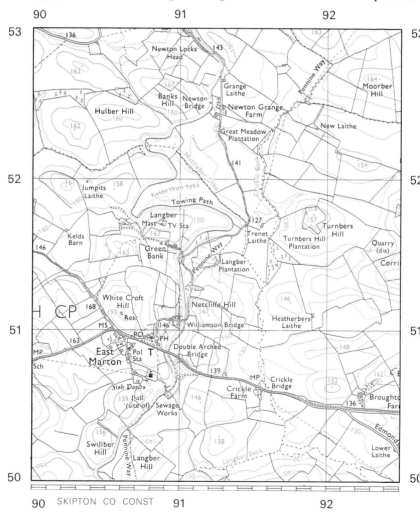

particular attention, and rocks are cut into
scenery of infinite variety and charm.
Coasts are fretted into tiny coves or major
bays depending on the nature and size of
any weakness, and the degree of exposure
to wave attack. The debris, sand or shingle,
or possibly both, accumulates at the head of
the cove or bay to form the beach.

Cliffs are further evidence of the sea in
destructive mood. Wave attack is restricted
to the zone of breaking waves. Here the
land is undercut and the rock above
collapses. This broken mass of rock defends
the land for a time, but is eventually
washed away by the waves which are then
free to renew their attack.

Undercutting, collapse, removal—the
cycle is repeated time and time again, and
the new-born cliff retreats inland, usually
gaining in height as it goes. The speed of
retreat depends on the strength of the rock.
At Land's End, the tough granite cliffs
stand firm and proud, and retreat with the
greatest reluctance. The weak boulder-clay
cliffs of Yorkshire's Holderness coast are
less determined. They pull back at an
average rate of a metre a year. Cliff retreat
usually leaves in its wake a shore composed

Massive slabs of broken
rock are neatly stacked by
waves breaking on the
headland of Filey Brig.

Horizontal layers of rock
are undercut and fretted
into a tiny cove on the
Yorkshire coast.

Fingal's Cave, Staffa, cut by the sea into a distinctive layer of ancient lava.

of flat tide-washed rock, indicated on the OS map by a distinctive symbol. Not suitable, perhaps, for sunbathing or swimming, these shores offer instead the attraction of many shallow rock pools which, with their quota of seaweeds and sea creatures, can keep the inquisitive fully absorbed for hours.

The fine detail of cliffed coastlines, which form such attractive backgrounds to many a holiday snap, is also the result of the work of the waves. A fault or crack in even the toughest rock is hollowed out into a cave. Other narrow weaknesses may be developed into long narrow inlets, often described as *geos*. Waves may drill a neat hole through a projecting headland to create a natural arch. As the land retreats, lumps of rock, tiny islands in fact, may be left behind to be consumed by the sea at its leisure. The most famous of these *stacks* are

At Flamborough Head, white chalk is capped by thick brown boulder clay left by a visiting ice sheet. Together they are carved by the sea into cove, cave, stack and arch.

The Needles off the south-west tip of the
Isle of Wight.

For coastlines, the larger scale of the
Pathfinder maps is a great advantage.
Coastal scenery is portrayed in great detail.
This will be appreciated from *extract 25*,
which shows part of the Atlantic coast of
Orkney. Examples of the features
mentioned above can be identified, and map
study enables us to build up a true mental
picture of, for instance, the view over the
Bay of Skaill.

The sea has moods other than the purely
destructive. It shifts and shapes the beach,
and constant wave activity smooths and

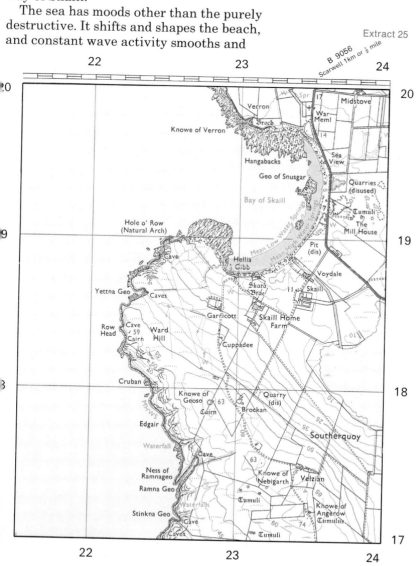

rounds the shingle. Sometimes it helps in the creation of new land, which is compensation for that which it takes away.

Constructive work

Beach material is constantly shifting. A wave which breaks obliquely drives sand and shingle up the beach at an angle, but the backwash drags it back on a line that is square to the coast. Thus, each wave may result in a slight lateral shift of beach material. When, driven by a prevailing wind, waves roll in mainly from one direction, the process can lead to the steady drift of sand and shingle along the shore. The authorities in many holiday resorts have equipped their beaches with groynes. These, indicated on the map by short black lines across the beach, are usually stout wooden walls. They check the longshore drift. Sand or shingle piles high on the windward side, but the beach is low to leeward, and the shelter so afforded is appreciated by holidaymakers on the windy sand-in-the-sandwich days which are all too common during the typical British summer.

Sometimes, the wave-driven drift of material extends the beach into open water to form a *spit*, such as the splendidly hooked example seen in *extract 26*. Hurst Castle which once defended the western

Extract 26

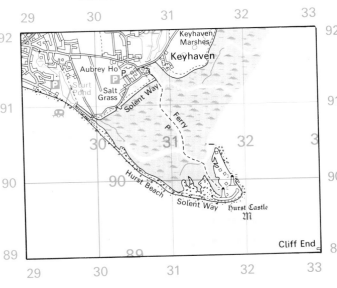

Tough marram grass struggles to hold in place the shifting sand. In the background lies another, older, line of dunes.

approach to the Solent, sits proudly on its seaward end.

The area behind a spit is a good site for the creation of new land. These quiet, sheltered waters receive river-borne muds which are colonised by plant life tolerant of a salty environment. These plants filter out more sediment from the slowly swirling waters. The sea becomes shallower as the land builds up, and salt marshes or saltings, shown on the map by their own symbol, are created. These wild wastes, beloved by seabirds, are washed by the higher tides and are cut by winding tidal channels. In time, they may be ripe for reclamation and the level land so created can be put to productive use.

Sand dunes, a feature of many lowland coasts, are the joint creation of sea and wind. On a windy day, when low tide exposes an extensive sandy beach, fine dry sand can be seen shimmering inland. It may come to rest, safe from the sea, on land that is above the level of the highest tides.

Salt marsh flanks the banks of the estuary of the River Conwy. The fishing vessel will be able to return to the sea when the highest tides flood the channel which presently serves as a convenient parking place.

It accumulates around any chance obstruction to be lumped into a dune. Colonised and anchored by tough grasses, it grows as new supplies of sand arrive on the wind. Sand dunes, which often occur in two or more roughly parallel lines, are marked on the map by name or symbol. The word 'warren' is further evidence, and coastal golf courses or links mark a fitting use for these lands of natural rough and bunker.

Changes in mean sea level

Mean sea level is not constant. It fluctuates in response to movements of the earth's crust, and the varying amounts of water locked away in the world's vast ice sheets, such as those of Antarctica. Today, for example, the mean level of the seas around south-east England is rising steadily. The rise per year is very, very small, but it has made necessary the construction on a defensive barrier across the River Thames. Through the OS map, we may identify some of the effects of changes in sea level in recent geological times. The multitude of estuaries and large bays that are a feature of Britain's coasts are a result of the considerable rise in sea level that has occurred in post-glacial times. As the sea level rose, the lower reaches of many rivers were effectively drowned. This produced the many winding, but often mud-choked, arms of the sea, which offer such tempting challenges to the many who love messing about in boats. In some areas, western Scotland for instance, the map, through its contours, records level coastal ledges often backed by fossil cliffs. These represent former beaches abandoned when the land was uplifted above mean sea level.

Occasionally the OS map records the presence of submarine forests. Here, at extreme low tide or after a storm, we may see the stumps and roots of trees which grew when the level of the sea was much lower. The rising seas brought death but not complete destruction.

Clay scenery

In many parts of Britain it is the nature and

The stump of an ancient tree, now dressed in seaweed, which formed part of a forest that flourished in times when the sea was well below its present level.

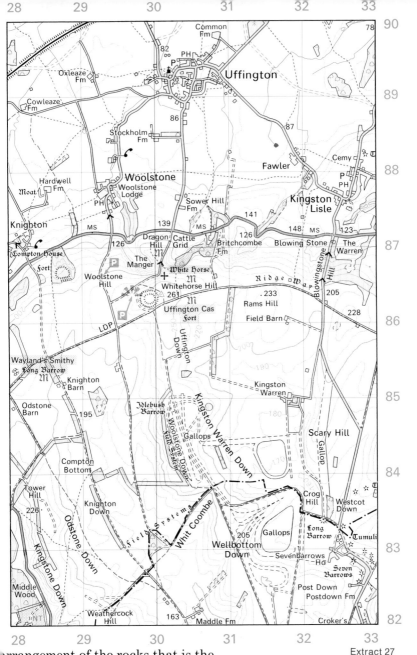

Extract 27

arrangement of the rocks that is the dominant factor in the creation of scenery. *Extract 27* provides illustration. To the north, this extract extends into the Vale of White Horse east of Swindon. North of the B-class road, the land is mainly underlain by clay, one of the weaker, less resistant rocks. Under attack from weathering and river action, the land surface has been reduced to a low and gentle plain which offers little contrast in elevation. The clay rock is watertight. Rain has no underground escape hatch, and so supports numerous rivers and streams.

Chalkland scenery
South of the B-class road, a different rock outcrops, and the contrast is most marked, not only in scenery but also in the use made of the land by man. Chalk is a sedimentary rock formed on the floor of a long-departed sea. In the course of crustal convulsion, this great thick layer of rock was uplifted. It was tilted slightly in the process and the exposed edge now forms the steep north-facing slope represented on the map by the close-packed contours which peak at the

The White Horse
at Uffington

Cherhill white horse,
Wiltshire.

The South Downs at
Upwaltham, West Sussex.

ummit of Whitehorse Hill (GR 301 864). To
he south, the slope of the land is much
nore gentle. This combination of slopes,
steep and gentle, scarp and dip, identifies a
najor landform feature known as a *cuesta*.
Much of the higher land of southern and
eastern England takes this form. The
Cotswolds, Chilterns and several Downs
nd Wolds are familiar examples.

Chalk is a thirsty rock. It absorbs into its
underground reservoirs nearly all the rain
hat falls. It liberates little to the demands
of surface flow. Streams in chalk are
relatively rare and are generally restricted
o valleys deep enough to tap supplies of
vater held deep in the rock. Rare they may
e, but they do have character and charm.
Clear and shallow, they meander through
neadows or beds of watercress, and often
rovide the fly fisherman with a state not
ar removed from paradise.

The dry slopes mapped in the southern

A dry valley cut into the chalk of the Yorkshire Wolds. Its level floor, once graced by a river, is now dry and productive farmland.

part of *extract 27* are more typical of chalkland country. There may be no streams, but contours reveal that valleys are abundant. In some earlier geological period different conditions must have prevailed for these valleys to have been excavated. Dry valleys give the dip slope its rolling, undulating surface, and scar the face of the scarp. This diversity of view, together with the dry, springy turf which clothes the hard white rock makes for pleasant walking.

The water held deep down in the rock often breaks out onto the surface where chalk meets an impermeable rock such as clay. This gives rise to the springs which are the source of many streams. Examples may be seen on the map along the foot of the scarp slope. The presence of constant supplies of clear, pure water encouraged the early farmers to settle on the sites of villages such as Kingston Lisle and Woolstone.

Limestone scenery

Of all the many different types of rock which contribute to the geological map of Great Britain, it is the limestone, dating back to the carboniferous period of the geological calendar, which gives rise to the

Gordale Scar, North Yorkshire.

most distinctive scenery. Formed some 300 million years ago, it outcrops to dominate the landscape over large areas of the Pennines, the plateau of Mendip, parts of south and north Wales, and the southern fringe of the Lake District. It is a sedimentary rock of great thickness made up of numerous layers or *strata*. Layer rests upon layer, and contact is marked by a *bedding plane*, a slight weakness, that is seized upon by natural processes in their efforts to destroy a rock that is otherwise tough and resistant. The drying out of the original sediments produced other lines of relative weakness. These are *joints*, which roughly cross at right angles. Imagine a high stack of huge chessboards and you may gain an impression of the pattern of weaknesses on which nature works. In carving limestone into scenery, nature has an additional powerful weapon—solution. Limestone, being composed mainly of calcium carbonate, is dissolved by acid, and rain is an acid, though very weak. Limestone does not dissolve like sugar in tea, but given a time-scale of millions of years, rainwater working on limestone can give dramatic results.

Limestone scenery, then, is greatly influenced by solution acting on a

Flowers and ferns shelter in a deep grike in a limestone pavement.

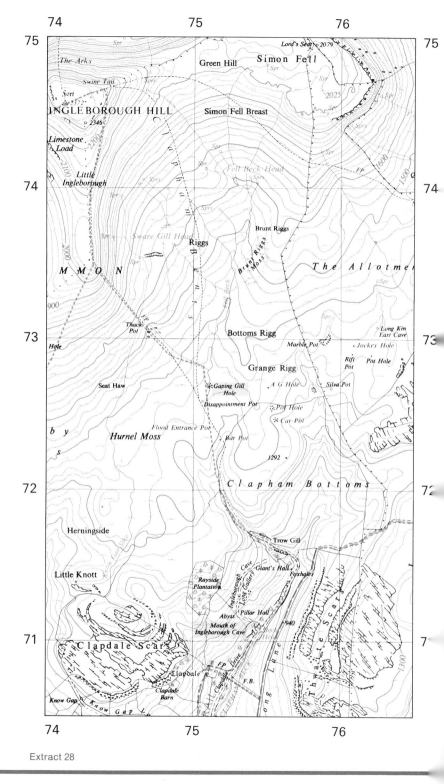

Extract 28

distinctive pattern of weaknesses. Clear illustration is provided by the *limestone pavement*. A layer of rock, bare and level, is under attack. The weaker joints have naturally suffered the greatest damage. They have been widened, and impressively deepened, into *grikes*, which isolate upstanding blocks of rock known as *clints*. A walk on a limestone pavement is a memorable experience. Stepping carefully from clint to clint we cross the deep grikes, which, sheltered from the wind and the ravages of grazing sheep, contain a flora of interest and distinction. The surface and sides of the clints are often carved into runnels and cavities by the power of solution.

The OS map locates limestone pavements by black shading. An example is seen in Clapdale Scars, *extract 28*, GR 745 710. This extract is taken from the Three Peaks 1:25 000 Outdoor Leisure Map. It portrays a tiny corner of the Craven district of North Yorkshire, just inside the Yorkshire Dales National Park. It shows many of the fascinating features of limestone scenery.

The southern half of the extract is mainly composed of limestone. It takes the form of a plateau, but its surface is deeply cut by dry valleys. To the north, the land which rises steeply to the shapely summits of Ingleborough Hill and Simon Fell is not composed of limestone, but of a series of other sedimentary rocks. Rainwater slowly makes its way through these rocks to emerge at the springs, which are indicated on this map by a little blue circle and the appropriate abbreviation—Spr. These springs are the source of the numerous small streams which are eventually gathered together to form Fell Beck. Know Gap Sike (GR 745 715), incidentally, may be ignored, for the eccentric manner in which it crosses the contour lines reveals it to be not a natural stream, but a man-made drainage channel.

Once upon a geological time, Fell Beck continued across the limestone plateau and eroded the valley, now dry, which is clearly indicated by the pattern of contours. But solution was at work as water seeped down the joints over which Fell Beck flowed. More water was diverted underground as the joints were enlarged. Eventually, one joint, the first encountered by Fell Beck as it crossed onto the limestone, was enlarged to such an extent that it was able to swallow up all the water that the stream could deliver. The result, prominently identified on the extract at GR 751 727, is Gaping Gill Hole, one of the many *swallow holes* which line the inner edge of the limestone plateau in this area.

Over the lip of Gaping Gill, Fell Beck tumbles more than 100 metres to become an underground river. Solution is as effective underground as it is on the surface. Water flowing along bedding places creates low, wide passages. Enlargement of joints gives vertical pitches. Locally, the rock is hollowed out into beautiful caverns, large and small, often decorated by roof-hung stalactites and floor-based stalagmites, which, in their arrangement, reflect the line of the joints down which the creative lime-rich waters have passed. Many underground passageways are now dry, for the water which created them has dissolved new and lower routes for itself. After an eventful journey, Fell Beck eventually returns to the light of day at Beck Head (GR 754 711), where the base of the limestone rests on rock which will support the surface flow of water.

Only the dedicated caver, with care and the appropriate equipment, can fully appreciate the beauty and complexity of these subterranean worlds. Less adventurous souls may gain a glimpse by visiting one of the more accessible caverns, such as Ingleborough Cave, which are open to the public.

Return now to daylight and the limestone plateau. Its surface is pockmarked by innumerable holes and hollows. Some, of course, are swallow holes. Others once had that status but have been abandoned by the river that gave them birth and, now dry, are marked on the map as pots or *pot holes*. Many hollows are due to the collapse of the

The deep cleft of Trow Gill, once the channel of an underground river.

surface as solution has removed the supporting limestone. Occasionally, the roof of a cavern may have collapsed and been washed away to leave a deep gash in the surface. Trow Gill (GR 755 716), with its towering walls marked by the scars left by scouring streams, is considered an example.

Granite scenery

Dartmoor, like the other moorlands which extend in decreasing size and height as far as the Isles of Scilly, is composed of granite. From any high vantage point, the land rolls to the horizon in a series of smooth, rounded summits separated by the wide and open valleys of many small streams. Often the underlying granite bursts through the summit surface to form the small but dramatic rock-castles known as *tors*. A typical example is seen in the photograph, which features Bowerman's Nose, Dartmoor. The granite stands proud and strong, but it bears the scars of frost in the enlarged joints that divide it into blocks.

Dartmoor, in common with all areas south of the line of the River Thames, never felt the weight of permanent ice, but during the ice age this high area lay close to the edge of the ice sheet. During the springs and autumns of those distant years,

Bowerman's Nose, Dartmoor.

Man makes his small contribution to this landscape near Abergwesyn, Powys.

temperatures fluctuated fiercely about the point of freezing. Water seeped into joints that had been produced when the rock originally cooled from its molten state. This water expanded when it was frozen into ice, and so outward pressure was exerted on the rock. Pressure, constantly repeated, eventually shattered the surface layer of granite on summit and spurs. Much debris was sludged downhill and away, but upstanding cores were left as the tors, which add such a distinctive touch to the Dartmoor landscape.

The work of man

Nature can seldom claim sole credit for Britain's beautiful scenery, for man has often made an impact which contributes to its appeal. A lonely whitewashed farmhouse, sheltering in an upland valley, introduces an attractive human touch to an otherwise stark natural landscape. Patches of woodland may soften a sharp, harsh skyline. Mature hedges are the framework for the subtle variations in colour and tone that results from man's agricultural use of the land.

In some areas man can claim full responsibility for the present-day landscape. The Fens which flank the Wash, together with smaller areas in Somerset,

Yorkshire and elsewhere, are uniquely man's creation. Nature provided the raw materials, but man did the constructive work. Shallow bays or arms of the sea were filled with sediment brought down by rivers. Peat developed to fill inland lakes and lagoons. The whole rose close to mean sea level. In their natural state these areas offered a watery environment, frequently flooded, at best no better than marsh.

For centuries, man has laboured hard to control the waters of river and sea and to create dry land to support his agriculture and settlement. The OS map plots with precision the steps he has taken. Sea walls or banks keep the sea at bay, sluggish meandering rivers are shortened by canals to increase their speed of flow and so hasten the discharge of water. Embankments, indicated on the map by hachures, defend the low-lying farmland from the danger of damaging floods. Rain can't flow over the level land, but drains instead into an intricate network of deep ditches. These, represented on the map by thin straight blue lines, add a distinctive element to the fenland map such as that from which *extract 29* on page 156 is taken. Ditches connect with larger drainage channels, and water must eventually be lifted up to canal or river for delivery to the sea. This is now the responsibility of modern pumps, but once it was the task of windmills, some of which remain to grace the landscape.

Fenland areas, as may be readily appreciated from the map, are monotonously level and low. Contours are rare. Occasional specimens are found marked with a zero, indicating that the land is at mean sea level. Only tiny areas, once islands in a shallow sea, are ringed by the 10 metres contour. Elsewhere we must turn to spot heights to determine the height of the land. In some cases these are preceded by a minus sign, showing that the land is actually lower than mean sea level.

The scenic view
The imprint of landscape processes is on hand for all to see. The gardener may curse

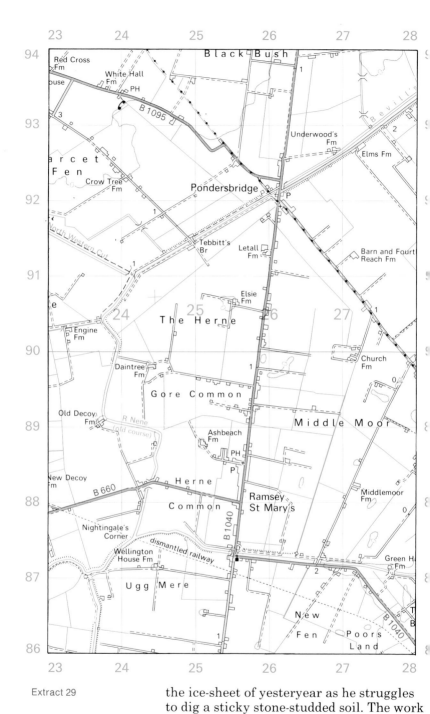

Extract 29

the ice-sheet of yesteryear as he struggles to dig a sticky stone-studded soil. The work of rivers is to be seen and appreciated not far from your front door. To view the more majestic results of natural sculpture, however, most of us must follow the map and venture a little further. Britain offers a wide variety of attractive destinations. Many of these are indicated as such on the map.

The ten National Parks of England and Wales are clustered on the older, tougher rocks of north and west. They are rich in scenic contrast. Snowdonia and the Lake District, for instance, have the natural beauty that stems from the work of glaciers. The Pembrokeshire coast offers a succession of magnificent sea-sculpted vistas. The Yorkshire Dales and the Peak District feature the distinctive scenery of limestone rock. Dartmoor offers rolling moorland wrapped in peace and solitude.

Lowland England, though lacking mountains and moors, is rich in scenic charm. It includes extensive tracts designated as 'areas of outstanding natural beauty'. The chalklands of Downs and Chilterns are prominent among them. So, too, are coastlands from Norfolk, through Dorset, to the extreme south-west. The natural beauty of the Cotswolds is heightened by the hand of man working with the local honey-coloured stone.

Scotland has no National Parks. Many would argue that most of Scotland *is* a national park. The greater part of the country, particularly the north and west, offers unrivalled scenery of mountain and coast. Exceptionally beautiful districts are highlighted as 'National Scenic Areas'.

Many areas of particular scenic beauty and interest have been bought by the National Trust in order to conserve and maintain them for the nation. Land owned by the Trust is clearly shown on the OS map by means of the 'NT' symbol ('NTS' in Scotland).

Whether specially designated or not, Britain's landscape, and its villages and towns, have much to offer. They are there for everyone to enjoy. All you have to do is follow the map.

Index